MY FAVORITE WAR STORY

My Favorite

WHITTLESEY HOUSE

*34 Dramatic Tales of Gallantry, of Intrigue, of Violence and
Espionage from the pages of LOOK Magazine, each told by a
Famous War Correspondent or Writer-Soldier, and chosen by him
as the most engrossing of all the War Stories he has encountered.*

War Story

COMPILED BY THE EDITORS OF LOOK

NEW YORK · LONDON · McGRAW-HILL BOOK COMPANY INC.

PREFACE

If there is anything a fighting man has done in this war that a war correspondent has failed to do, I do not know what it is. They have gone on commando raids. They have jumped with the first wave of paratroopers in every major invasion. They have crawled through the green slime of the New Guinea jungle, have frozen in the Huertgen forest. They have flown repeatedly over Berlin and Tokyo and the other targets that have blossomed with deadly flak.

They have not, of course, killed Germans or Japs. Under the Geneva convention they are forbidden to carry firearms. But they have died under fire, a great many of them, as the accompanying list shows. The number of war correspondents killed is far greater in proportion than the number of deaths among combat troops. That is because their own zeal to see it themselves, to be there when it happens, drives them into the face of danger.

If they have not killed Japs and Germans (and I wouldn't bet too much on that), they have made Americans back home understand what it means to be in the killing business. They have helped to bridge the vast gap between parents and wives who have known only the security and comfort of America and the men who have gone through the fearful hell of modern war.

Every war correspondent — even those of us who are properly described as trippers, passing briefly in and out of a theater of war — has had the experience of a letter from a father or mother in response to some story about a particular outfit: "Our Joe was with the Umpteenth Division . . . what you wrote made us feel what he was going through . . . the things he couldn't, or didn't, put into his letters . . ." Morale is an inadequate word. It covers a million and one things such as that kind of letter. And war correspondents have contributed immeasurably to understanding, which is a vital part of morale.

Battle reporters on the job have the hardboiled nonchalance of the fighting man. Outwardly they take themselves and their work with the utmost casualness. That, however, is largely a facade. They are adventure-loving, deeply sentimental and insatiably curious. If they weren't, of course, they would be writing about something a lot quieter and safer than war.

Often the job becomes an endurance contest. In Europe last winter you drove over icy roads in an open jeep in temperatures below zero. You drove fifty miles to get your story. Then you drove seventy-five miles to a press camp and tried to write it with freezing fingers for a deadline an hour away.

Like so much of war, the job of the war correspondent is often endlessly boring and repetitive. It is waiting and waiting and waiting. It is endless poker, and irritable wires from the managing editor back home, and a row with the censor. It means struggling with unhappy public relations officers who are responsible for the safety of correspondents and who have taken a great deal of punishment in this most completely covered of all wars.

The stories in this book have been drawn from every theater of war and every phase of warfare. Most of them deal with GIs — the men who do the actual fighting. War correspondents are by nature skeptical of the brass, suspicious of the big boys back at division headquarters.

Here are stories by some "big names." But it is surprising how many are signed by men at best known only vaguely to the general public. These stories have the same immediacy, the same urgency, as the work of the famous correspondents, for they all come out of the fire of experience.

Almost as interesting as the stories themselves are the brief biographical sketches of the reporters who set them down. Here, too, is a record of adventure. In plain, unvarnished language they tell of wanderings and perils in far places of the earth.

Much has been crowded into these terrible years of the war. Every day, every hour, every second some miraculous and incredible thing was happening. Here is a rare collection of extraordinary events, each chosen by a connoisseur out of his own personal experience of the miracles of bravery and of luck that have occurred endlessly in this fantastic time we are living through.

MARQUIS CHILDS
WASHINGTON, D. C.

IN LINE OF DUTY

These correspondents were killed during the Second World War:

John Andrew
Ralph Barnes
Irvin Bede
Lea Burdett
Asabel Bush
William Henry Chickering
Raymond Clapper
Harry E. Crockett
Frank J. Cuhel
Byron Darnton
Frederick Faust (Max Brand)
Jack Frankish
Stanley Gunn
Melville Jacoby
Harold W. Kulick
Lucien A. Labaudt
David Lardner
Gaston Madru
Webb Miller
Damien Parer
Harry L. Percy
Eugene Petrov
Robert P. Post
Frank Prist
Ernie Pyle
Ben Robertson
Jack Singer
Brydon Taves
John B. Terry
Carl Thusgaard
Tom Treanor

CONTENTS

MY FAVORITE WAR STORY

THE SPY'S LOST LOVE

by Martin Agronsky

Just off the Greek coast in the Aegean Sea there lies a group of small islands that overlook the entrance to the harbor of Piraeus, the port of Athens. On the islands live simple Greek fisherfolk.

In the spring of 1941, a few days after the R.A.F. began nightly bombing runs from Athens over Albania and Italy, the returning pilots started reporting that targets they had hoped to approach by surprise seemed dangerously alert to attack, ready to counter their blows.

Pilot after pilot reported to Squadron Intelligence that the flights were being regularly intercepted by Italian night fighters miles from their intended targets. They said that when they did arrive over the target area they found searchlights sweeping the skies and heavy ack-ack fire concentrated upon them.

At first this was attributed to the unprecedented excellence of the Italian antiaircraft detector system. But when these experiences were duplicated with unfailing and suspicious regularity, Squadron Intelligence decided that the Italians were getting warnings of approaching raids long before the best mechanical devices could have supplied them.

At approximately the same time, Intelligence also received reports of unidentified radio activity in the vicinity of Piraeus.

With the help of the Greek Military Intelligence, a search was made in the little islands. On all but one the investigators found only fishermen's poor huts and no radio equipment whatever. On the last island they found a sumptuous villa. It was occupied by a

15

The ending of the story is mysterious. The Italian had obviously killed

her, but the secret of how he disposed of her corpse he carried to his grave.

prosperous retired Greek merchant.

The merchant's villa, too, was searched, as well as a chapel he had built in memory of his recently deceased young wife. The agents found nothing.

On the mainland, while investigating the merchant's background, the agents heard a tragic story. The merchant, villagers told them, had returned to Greece a few years before with a fortune made in America. He had married one of the beauties of the neighborhood and built the villa for himself and his bride.

Then, only a few months before Italy's attack on Greece, the young wife had died suddenly. Heartbroken, the man immediately had a chapel constructed in her memory. He refused to permit her burial. Instead, she was embalmed and her body was placed in an elaborate coffin in the new chapel.

Meanwhile, the activity of the unidentified radio station operating near Piraeus continued. The agents were stumped.

Then, so the story goes, an old maidservant of the wealthy widower informed the authorities that her master went nightly to his wife's chapel and that mysterious sounds came from within while he was there. This time the agents in their search almost took the chapel apart. Again they found nothing. Then they decided to open the beautiful young girl's coffin.

Inside it they found, as you may have suspected, a very powerful and elaborate sending and receiving set. The wealthy widower, as you also must have guessed, was identified as an able Italian spy. He was duly executed.

And, since this is a Balkan story, it has its mysterious ending. No one, so a British agent informed me, ever found the body of the lovely young bride whose place was taken by a radio set. The Italian spy obviously had killed her. But the secret of how he disposed of her corpse he carried to his grave.

18

Martin Agronsky

Martin Agronsky was educated in Philadelphia and at Rutgers University.

After graduation, he went to Palestine, where he joined the Palestine Post in Jerusalem. He remained for more than a year, acting as a correspondent for the Christian Science Monitor, International News Service and Newsweek magazine.

Agronsky returned to the U.S for a brief visit in 1938, then sailed for Italy, where he did a series of articles for the magazine, Foreign Affairs, and served for a time in the Paris bureau of INS. Later he covered the Spanish Civil War for the Chicago Tribune and the London News-Chronicle.

His first radio broadcast was made from Geneva, Switzerland, in December, 1939, and until September, 1942, he was a National Broadcasting Company correspondent in that city and in Belgrade, Budapest, Bucharest, Athens, Sofia and Ankara.

Agronsky was a war correspondent with the British Army in Libya and with the British expeditionary forces in Greece and Singapore. He also broadcast a number of times from General MacArthur's headquarters in Australia.

In 1942, Rutgers University presented him, in absentia, with an award, a bronze medal, for "fearless and searching interpretation of world events."

Since March, 1943, he has been Washington correspondent for the Blue Network, broadcasting six days a week.

19

THE SCHOOLTEACHER CHOOSES DEATH

by Frederic S. Marquardt

Of all the Filipinos I have known, Buenaventura J. Bello seemed the least likely to become a hero. He used to visit the *Free Press* office in Manila, a diffident little fellow of the older generation. He always wore a black bow tie, and his white linen suits were immaculately clean, although often threadbare.

He would walk quietly across the news room and stand beside my desk until I looked up and recognized him. Then he'd flash that friendly grin of his and, no matter how close a deadline might be, I'd pull up a chair and ask him to sit down.

Bello was about forty years old. He was a poet in Ilocano, one of the principal dialects of northern Luzon, and a good many of his poems had been published. Like most Filipinos, he believed in big families and was very proud of his six children.

A school teacher, he was also proud of his profession. But he was even more proud of the Philippine public school system.

"Our schools are the greatest monuments to the United States in the Philippines," he often said to me. "No matter what the future holds for the Filipino people, no one can destroy the seeds of democracy that the American public school system has implanted in our breasts."

It sounds a little like an oration, as I put it down on paper, but most Filipinos are orators, anyway, and no one who heard Bello could doubt his sincerity.

Often, he brought in articles that he wanted me to publish. I wish now that I had accepted more of them. But they seemed

Bello shook his head. The little Jap officer with the big sword was enraged. "Give him two minutes, then shoot him if he still refuses!"

pretty academic in those pre-Pearl Harbor days. They were usually on such subjects as *Democracy in the Philippines, Man Lives Not by Bread Alone* and *Independence — Goal of American-Filipino Co-operation.*

Once, Bello asked me to act as a judge at an oratorical contest in his school. But Vigan was a long way from Manila, so I took the easy way out and donated a prize, instead. It was a volume of famous American orations, and included Patrick Henry's immortal "Give me liberty, or give me death!"

I wasn't in the Philippines when the Japs moved in, but Bello was, and the story of his heroism was brought out by the handful of fortunate American and Filipino soldiers who managed to escape from Bataan.

By the time the little men from Dai Nippon reached Vigan, the schools had been officially closed and the children told to stay in their homes. But habit is strong, and the doughty master had gone to his school as usual that morning. He ran up the American and Filipino flags on the twin bamboo poles in front of the school, humming *The Star Spangled Banner* and the Philippine national anthem. Then he sat down on the school steps to wait for the onrushing Japanese juggernaut.

He didn't have to wait long. First came the motorcycle patrols and a couple of light tanks; then troop-carrying buses; and finally a command car. This was what Bello had been waiting for.

The Jap officer saw the school flags and ordered his auto stopped. Bello rose and started toward the car, his politeness instinctively overcoming his hatred for the invader.

"You!" the Jap officer ordered. "Pull down that American flag!"
Bello shook his head.

"I can't," he answered simply.

"We are not fighting you Filipinos," the Jap said ingratiatingly. "Our only enemy is the American. We have come to save you from the hated white man. You may fly the Philippine flag. But you must tear down the American flag."

Again Bello shook his head.

"No," he said.

22

The little Jap officer with the big sword shouted in rage, "Give him two minutes, then shoot him if he still refuses to tear down the American flag!"

No one knows what passed through Bello's mind during those 120 seconds. I'd wager that Patrick Henry was in his thoughts, as well as the six children to whom he was leaving a heritage more precious than rice lands.

I'd bet he thought of the school system, and of the American nation-building experiment that proved an Asiatic subject-people could be raised to the status of independence.

Then a shot echoed across the schoolyard, and Bello fell beneath the American and Filipino flags fluttering briskly against the blue tropical sky. His last wish, I feel certain, was that his six children, someday, would see those flags again flying side by side over Philippine soil.

Frederic S. Marquardt

Frederic S. Marquardt, chief of the Southwest Pacific Area for OWI, returned to his home town when he went into the Philippines with General MacArthur. Marquardt was born in Manila in 1905.

Marquardt traveled widely in the Far East after graduating from Hamilton College in 1927, and was assistant editor of the Philippine Free Press *from 1928 to 1941. Later, he was cable editor of the Chicago* Sun.

In the OWI, he is producing written and spoken material for psychological warfare.

Marquardt has lectured, written many magazine articles and one book, Before Bataan and After.

COUNTERESPIONAGE IN BUCHAREST

by Robert St. John

It happened in Bucharest, during the period known as "the war of nerves," just before the Nazis swept into the Balkans. King Carol was still clinging to his shaky throne—and Magda Lupescu was clinging to Carol—but everyone knew that revolution was brewing in Rumania. Everyone knew that Carol didn't have long to last. And everyone knew that the Balkans didn't have long to last, either.

Everyone had the jitters. The atmosphere was tense, all of the time, and people spoke in whispers.

None of us ever threw a letter into a wastebasket, even though it was torn to bits, because we all knew that the chambermaids were selling the contents of hotel wastebaskets to the Gestapo for fancy prices.

The main job we foreign correspondents had was sifting fact from fantasy. The sidewalk cafes were abuzz, night and day, with rumors that had been planted there by foreign agents.

Rumania, on the verge of a sellout to Hitler, was more corrupt than ever. You could "buy" anyone in public office, from the Prime Minister down to the lowliest police officer. Some of us foreign correspondents even had palace attendants on our pay roll—men who, when the German minister called, actually supplied us with stenographic transcripts of what he said to Carol. And we all had officers in the Rumanian Secret Police who sold us a miscellaneous mess of information for a price that was cheap.

You must understand this, or my story won't seem plausible. And it IS a true story.

The chief character was a man known throughout the Balkans as

By the time he reached the last page, Dominick's fingers were trembling. Then, suddenly, his face went white. He leaped from his chair.

25

Dominick the Levantine, a slippery individual who dressed elegantly and drove the most expensive American cars. He always carried an ivory-headed cane, and when you asked him if it were true that the cane contained a phial of poison, as well as a thin blade of steel, Dominick only grinned and stroked his drooping mustachios.

How he lived in such style was no mystery to us correspondents. We all knew his business was selling military and political secrets— Rumanian secrets to Bulgaria . . . Bulgarian secrets to Turkey . . . Turkish secrets to Greece.

The state police were always after him, but Dominick continued to go his slithery way, cocksure, arrogant. They tried to trap him, over and over again, with beautiful women and planted evidence, but Dominick always skipped free.

One day he even went so far as to offer a member of the secret police—a man who several times had done him favors, for a consideration—200,000 lei (about $400) for just a glimpse at the dossier containing his police record. Dominick explained that he was curious to see how much the secret police actually did know about him. He said he was also curious to find out if any of the people he'd trusted had been stool pigeons. The officer finally agreed, but he insisted that Dominick could have only half an hour to look the dossier over.

And so it was arranged. At eleven o'clock one night the two men met in the back room of a *bodega* directly across the street from police headquarters. The officer had brought the file there, and would wait to take it back. But before he gave up the thick dossier he insisted on having his 200,000 lei. Dominick handed over a roll of paper money, then eagerly opened the file. The officer put his watch on the table and kept glancing at it as he counted the bills.

As Dominick flicked the pages a smirk of satisfaction creased his face. He wasn't surprised to find transcripts of his telephone conversations, even hour-by-hour reports of his movements.

But several times his complacency vanished as he saw evidence that people he trusted had betrayed him. One of them was the mistress of a cabinet member in whom he had confided. On one page he found, pieced together, a letter he was certain he had destroyed.

By the time he reached the last page, his fingers were trembling. His *savoir faire* was all but gone.

Then, suddenly, his face went white. He leaped from his chair and ran to the window. He was about to throw it open when he saw two officers waiting alertly just outside, their eyes on that window. In a burst of fury, Dominick wheeled on the man in the room. But the officer was too quick for him. He flung open the door. In rushed men in uniform, who had been waiting outside for just that signal.

The dossier was still on the table, open to the last page. On it appeared this entry:

> NOVEMBER FIFTH: *Today Dominick the Levantine arranged to pay Vasile Milanescu 200,000 lei to inspect his dossier. The agreement will be carried out. Then punishment befitting his many acts of high treason against Rumania will be imposed on Dominick the Levantine.*

It was. Dominick was executed.

Robert St. John

This 42-year old reporter has survived a ship explosion in World War I, a shooting by Chicago gunmen, the London Blitz, the bombing of Belgrade in World War II. In 1939, assigned by the Associated Press to cover the war, St. John saw the Nazi terror march from Poland through the Balkans to Greece. Strafed by Nazi planes and wounded, he escaped from Yugoslavia in a fishing smack. Back in the United States, St. John is now a radio commentator for NBC. He is the author of From the Land of Silent People, *a reporter's account of Hitler's rape of the Balkans, and a novel,* It's Always Tomorrow.

HARA-KIRI IN JAPAN

by Robert Bellaire

In Tokyo, before Pearl Harbor, I knew Saburo Saito as an English-speaking radio propagandist—and a fanatical disciple of Seigo Nakano, the so-called "Hitler of Japan." Nakano, leader of the Tohokai Party Blue Shirts and a most dangerous Japanese jingoist, was too hot for even most Japanese to handle. I wanted an interview with him and I asked Saito to arrange it. After weeks of delay, he took me to party headquarters.

Three blue-shirted bodyguards, wearing Nazi armbands, searched me in an outer room. I had to surrender my pocketknife and fountain pen, which they promised to return after the interview.

"A word of caution," Saito warned me. "Do not forget that you are entering the presence of The Leader. In all the world, only the Emperor is more holy."

As I entered his office, alone, Nakano bolted to his feet, gave a stiff Nazi salute and cried: "Hail Nakano! Down with America and Britain!" I replied with "Good afternoon," and sat down.

Nakano was a short, wiry man with a Hitlerian mustache. His face was long and thin, his forehead high, his oily hair smoothly brushed back. Directly behind him was a picture of Emperor Hirohito, flanked by pictures of Hitler and Mussolini.

On his desk lay a long, highly polished Samurai sword, and beside it a short hara-kiri dagger. Nakano followed my eyes.

"I observe that your first interest is in this sword and dagger," he began, "rather than in what I may say. You are right. The sword is more important than words. I am sick of words."

Suddenly Seigo Nakano was on his feet, swinging the sword over his head as if to slice me in half. For a moment his face was bright crimson.

29

As he spoke, Nakano took up the sword and tenderly fingered its razor-sharp edge. I had seen Japanese army officers in China behead Chinese prisoners with a single swing of these weapons.

"Words are the harmless weapon of your decadent democracies," he said. "But your country shall perish when Japan lifts the sword!"

Suddenly he was on his feet, swinging the sword over his head as if to slice me in half. For a moment his face turned bright crimson. Then he recovered himself and lowered the sword, placing it on his desk. Meantime I had said nothing.

"Japan has been given a holy mission," he said at last. "The peoples of the world have strayed far from their true spiritual leader, our Holy Emperor of the Universe. Japan must force them, for their own good, to accept the Emperor's leadership. I have been put on earth to lead this holy mission. That is my destiny!"

Nakano waved his hand to silence me as I began to say something.

"This is the time for boldness," he continued in an excited voice. "Japan should strike out in all directions—Manila, Singapore, Australia, California, India. We should push from this side of the world and Germany from the other, to meet at Suez, Moscow and Panama. That would seal the fate of Democracy and Communism. And in the next generation Japan could complete her holy mission by defeating Germany.

"Then the world would have eternal peace."

I asked whether he thought Japan was strong enough to hope to win such a war.

"Yes! Yes! Your democracies are only full of words. Your people will not die for their country. They have nothing for which to fight, and nothing with which to fight. You shall see! Japan will probably strike even before I become premier. . . ."

As I left the office I found Saito waiting.

"Now I hope you understand why more Japanese every day are becoming followers of The Leader," he said. "I would gladly give my life for him."

After Pearl Harbor, of course, I never saw Saito again. But I heard his broadcasts. He was still at it the night of October 28, 1943, almost 23 months after Pearl Harbor. That night he was reading a

30

bulletin describing a special session of the Japanese parliament at which Premier General Tojo had admitted that Japan had been forced on the defensive by America.

Suddenly Saito's voice broke. After several minutes a new voice continued: "We regret to announce the death in Tokyo tonight of Seigo Nakano, leader of the Tohokai Party and for 19 years a member of parliament. Mr. Nakano took his own life, according to Samurai tradition, after today's session of parliament."

Saito's broadcasts have not been heard since. I wonder: did he follow The Leader for whom he said he would die?

Robert Bellaire

Author, foreign correspondent and radio commentator, Robert Bellaire, a native of Iowa, was head of the United Press bureau in China in 1937 and in Japan three years later. In Shanghai, he narrowly escaped death three times in as many weeks when his apartment and office were bombed by Jap-inspired terrorists and when a 1,000-pound bomb—a dud—landed within 15 feet of him.

On the day of Pearl Harbor, the Japs threw Bellaire into "the worst prison in Japan." From behind bars he witnessed the Doolittle raid on Tokyo; he was tortured, threatened with death for his refusal to broadcast Japanese propaganda to the United States; he was accused of espionage and escaped a probable death sentence when he was exchanged as a prisoner of war on the Gripsholm late in 1942.

Since his return to the United States, he has lectured on Japan at *leading universities, at Army and Navy camps, and before hundreds of civilian audiences. He has also been on temporary duty with the Army Air Forces.*

FLYING BLIND

by Moscrip Miller

It was on my way back from China that I heard my favorite story of the war.

Several of General Chennault's fighter pilots, going home on the rotation plan, were shooting the breeze over some of the local vintage. Lieutenant Colonel Edward D. McComas, an old-time Chennault ace at 26 and commanding officer of the Black Lightning Squadron, was talking with fatherly pride of "his boys." Here is the story:

Twenty-one-year-old Captain John E. Meyer of Birmingham, Alabama, with four Jap planes to his credit, was leading a flight of P-51's—all that could be mustered that morning—in a raid on Jap shipping at Kurkiang. The ack-ack was heavy as the planes, flying in formation, dropped their bombs on the target with precision, then swung around in a 180-degree turn, banking sharply, to go back and finish the job with low-level strafing.

It was on the steeply banked turn that a 40 mm. shell hit the nose of Meyer's ship, exploding on impact and blinding the young pilot with shattered glass. Miraculously, he was not killed—but his plane was falling out of control as he calmly called over the inter-flight radio, "I'm out of it, boys. That hit blinded me. Polish off the —— for me, will you?"

But Meyer's wingman, Lieutenant John F. Egan, also just 21, from Fort Lauderdale, Florida, had other ideas. Sizing up the situation quickly, he called to Meyer, the only casualty of the bomb run, to follow his instructions.

Meyer was too shaken and weak from loss of blood to do more than follow blindly the radioed instructions that kept ringing in his ears. Egan was his eyes.

As Egan gave the orders by radio, the blinded Meyer, responding almost automatically, pulled back on the stick while bringing his left wing up, and leveled the falling plane. But then the blind pilot faced a new threat—from a flight of Jap Tojos and Oscars coming in to finish off the cripple.

The alert Egan saw them and called a warning. He had Meyer continue on course, but the other planes of his flight rallied around the crippled ship, as if they were running interference in a football game. One Jap fighter came in close, hosing lead as he came, but Meyer's interference knocked him out of the game. The other Japs hesitated, in spite of their numerical advantage, and that hesitation saved Meyer again.

Egan was now flying side by side with his blinded pal, keeping up a steady stream of conversation over the radio.

"How you doing, Stinky? This ought to be a cinch for you. You always were good at blind flying, and this is it—but good! More right rudder there. Nose down a bit. You're doing fine. The rest of the boys sure discouraged the hell out of those Nips. Only another half hour and we'll be home."

It was a one-sided conversation. Meyer was too weak from loss of blood, too shaken to do more than blindly follow the instructions that kept ringing in his ears. His handling of the controls was automatic and needed no sight. Egan was his eyes. Vaguely, he wondered if he were dead and his spirit flying on. Then he heard Egan talking to the control tower at the home field.

"Meyer is hit, blinded, but he's going to land his plane."

They were going to land. The realization roused Meyer.

Once around the field with half flaps into the wind. . . . Egan was calling out the air speed and altimeter readings as he flew alongside Meyer. Then the ground came up gently to meet the approaching planes. Egan guided the sightless pilot squarely onto the runway. At the last minute, he gunned his own plane upward again, just before his wheels touched earth. He circled the field and came in again—on the runway this time, instead of at the side as had been necessary when bringing in Meyer.

Warned in advance by the control tower, medics were waiting

for Meyer; he had been taken away by the time Egan landed.

Eventually, Meyer was to regain his sight.

But two days later, while Meyer was resting in a hospital, Jack Egan was lost over Hong Kong.

Moscrip Miller

Moscrip Miller wears the victory ribbon of World War I, in which he served 27 months as a volunteer ambulance driver.

He was born in Scotland just before the turn of the century, son of a Scots mother and an American father. The family settled in Battle Creek, Michigan, a year later.

Miller was graduated from Northwestern University after serving in the first World War. He then worked for the Chicago Tribune, *later edited a weekly magazine in Florida, in 1927 went to France and the Paris edition of the New York* Herald.

In 1932 he joined the staff of the New York Journal, *covering strikes, floods, murders, political investigations. Six years later, he went to work for the National Broadcasting Company as director of magazine feature publicity.*

In December, 1942, he joined the Office of War Information, trained the first OWI Psychological Warfare group to go overseas and followed it to North Africa.

Returning to this country in the spring of 1943, Miller became associated with LOOK, was sent overseas to the China-Burma-India theater.

In the Orient, he wrote a series of stories on the men of the 20th Bomber Command, made a crossing of the Hump, arrived at Kunming during a Jap air raid, and, with LOOK photographer Frank Bauman, interviewed Chiang Kai-shek.

"SIR, WILL IT HURT VERY MUCH?"

by Lt. Col. Vincent Sheean

On the night of August 1, 1943, the port of Palermo was sub-
jected to a singularly determined and persistent German
bombing raid. The hill of Santa Rosalia, west of Palermo, appeared
to be the beginning of the bomb run in at least two of the attacks.
Our Air Support Command, to which I was attached, had its headquarters and living quarters on that hill, commanding a superb
view of the harbor, bay and town.

Down in the harbor was the destroyer *Mayrant,* which had
come limping in only three days before after being dive-bombed
at sea. It had been badly damaged and was now immobile; we all
wondered how it had ever reached port.

A day or so before, the *Mayrant's* young executive officer had
asked me to help him acquire supplies of fresh water for his men.
Thanks to our friends of the Third Division, who always knew
how to get water or any other commodity, his ship was supplied.

On the night of August 1, JU-88's roared down over the city,
straight for the port, which was brilliantly illuminated by all the
fireworks of a night attack. There were red flares and white ones,
the flash of guns, the sight and sound of great explosions. I thought
of the *Mayrant* often during those hours. The ship was in no
condition to stand a near miss—much less a hit.

Next morning I went down to the port to get some naval esti-
mate of the damage, to put in our own reports. The *Mayrant* was
still afloat, though bombs had landed none too far away. I found
the young executive officer, who had just been able (at 9 a. m.)

36

Picking up the wounded sailor, the executive officer carried him down the treacherously narrow and steep ladders during the height of the raid.

to get out of his dirty and bloodstained uniform of the night before and put on a clean one. We went to breakfast in the wardroom and there I got a comprehensive account of what had happened.

They had fired their guns all through the two hours and a half of the attack, of course. The young officer was in command that night, as he was on alternate nights; the ship's skipper was on shore at naval headquarters.

The bombing of a few days before had so seriously damaged this destroyer that it had no adequate sick bay. The question of how to care for the wounded was serious. The executive officer, standing beside a gunner when a bomb fragment blew the latter's leg off, picked the boy up and started down the ladder.

Those ladders on a destroyer are bad enough in broad daylight. I can hardly get up or down them under the best of conditions. The officer carried the wounded sailor down two of these narrow, steep ladders, right smack in the middle of the raid, and then across two more ships alongside, to a third, which had adequate medical supplies and doctors.

In the intermittent glare and gloom of the night, in the broiling chaos of battle, it was an astounding feat. I traversed the route: it was all I could do to get over those rails and up and down those ladders and over all manner of other obstacles. The officer said that he did it by thinking of only one step at a time: not of his destination, but just of the next step.

Then he added: "Before I undertook the trek, I said to the sailor: 'We've got to get to a ship that has a hospital. I've got some morphine here. I'll give you a shot of that, son, and then we'll start.'

"The gunner had lost one leg and was wounded in the other; but this seemed really to shake him.

" 'Sir,' he said, 'will it hurt very much?' "

You've heard of this young executive officer before. His name is Franklin D. Roosevelt, Jr.

Lt. Col. Vincent Sheean

Sheean has a genius for being on the spot when world-shaking events are about to explode. He arrived in Italy on the day of the Fascist March on Rome in 1922; he saw and reported the Riff War, the national revolution in China in 1927, the Arab-Zionist riots in Palestine in 1929, the Civil War in Spain. He was in Czechoslovakia at the time of the Munich crisis, observing the events that were leading to the outbreak of World War II.

Sheean was in England during the blitz; he was in the Far East just before the attack on Pearl Harbor. He tells of his experiences up to the time of the fall of France in his book, Between the Thunder and the Sun.

Forty-five years old, a native of Pana, Illinois, Sheean attended the University of Chicago and started his career on the Chicago Daily News, transferring shortly afterward to the New York Daily News.

In the spring of 1922 he went abroad, and from that point on he acted as a foreign correspondent, both on regular assignments and as a free-lance writer.

During his years abroad he wrote two non-fiction best-sellers, Personal History and Not Peace but a Sword. His other books include two historical novels, Sanfelice and Day of Battle, and a collection of short stories, The Pieces of a Fan. He has written many magazine articles and translated Eve Curie's Madame Curie from the French.

When this country entered the war, Sheean joined the Army Air Forces. As an Intelligence officer, he took part in the invasion of North Africa; he was in the Sicilian campaign and in the early stages of the Italian campaign, and subsequently went to the Far East. In November, 1944, he was honorably discharged, with the rank of lieutenant colonel.

Acting as a foreign correspondent for the North American Newspaper Alliance, Redbook and the Blue Network, Sheean thereupon joined the American Third Army on the Western Front.

G.I. JOES AND AN ARAB STEAK

by Inez Robb

Americans do not really fight wars for souvenirs. It only seems that way. But somewhere in Italy, probably, are three American buck privates who jointly own one of the rarest souvenirs of the African campaign: a genuine, guaranteed authentic, 24-carat signature of the unapproachable Sultan of Morocco — the sacred Sidi Mohammed.

The trio obtained the autograph by no fanatical frontal attack on the person of the Sultan. They came to possess it through a transaction involving a very dead cow, $60 in cash, an anguished and vocal Arab and a brush with Moroccan justice.

The G.I. Joes had been in Morocco feeding on Army groceries sufficiently long to yearn—nay, to drool—passionately for a thick, juicy steak, with or without French fries.

Always the American dream has led to action, and these boys were not the ones to sit around and do nothing about their longings. So they went out one day and killed an Arab cow, a dead giveaway that the trio was composed of city boys. For no G.I. from Texas or Iowa would ever have killed one of those diminutive, thin-ribbed cows expecting to harvest anything but fourth-grade hamburger.

While they were skinning their prize, the three were caught red-handed, both literally and figuratively, by its ragged owner, who set up such a wail as only an outraged Arab, mourning a cash loss, can produce.

Moroccan gendarmes arrived pronto, arrested the G.I.'s and carried them off to jail. Prompt justice fined them $60 for their lawless

40

The three G.I. Joes were caught red-handed by the cow's ragged owner,
who set up such a wail as only an Arab, mourning a cash loss, can produce.

appetites. It was now the turn of the G.I. Joes to howl with anguish. But they paid up, consoling themselves with the thought that at least they would have a steak, and that steaks in Morocco were worth 20 bucks apiece.

But alas! Both cash and carcass were awarded to the bereaved Arab, and the trio returned to camp to face still more music. However, punishment was not severe, because some of the company officers who hailed from cow country argued that no herd of Arab cows, much less one critter, was worth $60.

For the next ten days the three chastened Joes stuck to camp, too broke to go into town. Then came the day of unexpected triumph. There was delivered to them at camp an impressive native document. On scrutiny it turned out to be a government receipt for the $60, but a receipt signed by the Sultan himself!

From the depths, they were catapulted to the heights. For a trifling inconvenience and a mere $60—3,000 francs at the current rate of exchange—they were in possession of the sacrosanct Sultan's autograph, a souvenir no other G.I. could boast.

Within 10 minutes, the three could have sold their trophy at a smart profit. As days went by, the ante went up. But the Joes steadfastly refused to sell. Today their souvenir reposes in the regimental safe.

Just how they will share their jointly owned autograph when the war is over is another problem.

And maybe, even, another war!

Inez Robb

Inez Callaway Robb, vivacious, veteran newspaperwoman, was born on a cattle ranch in California.

She attended the University of Idaho and the School of Journalism at·the University of Missouri. Upon graduation, she went to Tulsa, Oklahoma, and worked for the Tulsa Daily World. Then — with the impetuousness that is part of her nature —Inez hopped East and joined the staff of the New York Daily News.

During her 12 years at the News, her assignments included the coronation of King George VI and the wedding of the Duke and Duchess of Windsor.

Quoting Mrs. Robb: "Then I came to work for the International News Service and have been living the happy life of a whirling dervish ever since. I was among the reporters who traveled with the King and Queen of England during their six-weeks' tour of Canada and the United States; made the first round-trip flight across the Atlantic when Pan-American Airways inaugurated its European service in the summer of 1939; was spending the weekend at Cliveden when I heard the news of the Japanese attack on Pearl Har-

bor; stayed on in England to do a series on that nation at war, and went over to Ireland to do a story on the arrival of the first contingent of the A.E.F. in World War II."

In January, 1943, she sailed to Africa with the first overseas group of WACs.

Says Mrs. Robb: "I am the reporter who has never written a book. But I have a title: Ink Stained Wench."

VOUZA, SUPERMAN OF THE SOLOMONS

by Richard Tregaskis

My favorite war story concerns a certain Melanesian superman, a native of Guadalcanal. In a small way—like most Melanesians he is only five feet tall—this middle-aged native is the closest approach to the fictional character Tarzan that I have seen. This is the story of one of his superhuman feats.

His name is Vouza—simply that—although he likes to append the letters O.B.E., which stands for Officer of the British Empire, given him for 25 years of meritorious service as a police boy in the Guadalcanal-Tulagi area.

Vouza is short, broad of shoulder, and ironchested. He is the color of black coffee and his abdomen, exposed above a brief loincloth, is a washboard of muscle. His kinky hair is grizzly—for he is more than 50 years old—and his jaw has a determined set. His nose is flat and his forehead recedes. On his neck and reaching across the underside of his jaw, Vouza carries a long pink scar. How he got it is part of this tale.

For years before the war, a certain carpenter lived on Tulagi and practiced his trade. He was a solidly-built little Jap and his name was Ishimoto. Occasionally he would leave Tulagi for long jaunts which covered much of the Solomons. The truth is that Ishimoto was a Japanese agent, a major in the Japanese Army.

While Ishimoto was playing his double game, Vouza was working contentedly, quieting the boisterous natives of Guadalcanal.

When the Americans landed on that island, Vouza, who had been hiding in the hills during the Jap occupation, came down to our

Vouza still would not talk. One squat Jap gave him a tentative jab with a bayonet. "Talk!" shouted Ishimoto, but Vouza maintained his silence.

camp with an ancient Lee-Enfield rifle on his shoulder and offered his services as a scout. Seeing that he was wise to the bush, the Americans accepted his offer gladly and gave Vouza charge of a group of native scouts. They also gave him a small American flag. Thereafter, Vouza went on a scouting mission to Koli Point, east of Henderson Field, and there met Ishimoto.

Ishimoto had landed with some 1100 Japanese troops and was planning a drive to retake the airfield. His men caught Vouza off guard and captured him. In his loincloth the Japs found his small American flag, and Ishimoto ordered Vouza to tell what he knew of the American positions.

Vouza refused. Ishimoto thereupon had him hung up by the arms from the limb of a tree. When Vouza still would not talk, one squat Jap gave him a tentative jab with a bayonet.

"Talk!" Ishimoto shouted.

Vouza maintained his silence. Irritated, Ishimoto made a violent gesture with his hand and another Jap gouged Vouza's chest. Ishimoto cajoled and threatened, he bragged of what he would do, but Vouza would say nothing of the Americans on Guadalcanal. Ishimoto grew furious. Echoing his mood, one Jap bayoneted Vouza's throat and blood spurted from the gash.

Even that failed to loosen the native's tongue, and Ishimoto, frustrated, went off with his men, leaving Vouza hanging limply. But this did not mean they had finished with Vouza. They were confident that when they came back in the morning they would find him exhausted, wracked by torture, and ready to talk.

But when they did return they found only frayed rope ends where Vouza had been. During the night he had pulled himself up and, with his strong white teeth, had gnawed through the ropes.

Bleeding from his wounds, Vouza made his way to our lines on the Tenaru River. A doctor in Marine green sewed up his throat and in a few days he was out of the hospital. He then led our forces to the rear of the Japs, where we surprised them, and seized most of their artillery and much of their ammunition and food. Vouza happily watched the destruction of Japanese food stores, the burning of the native village where the Japs lived, and delighted in the sound

46

of the explosions as one of Ishimoto's ammunition dumps went up in an orange-fanged black cloud.

To make the story complete, Ishimoto subsequently led his troops in an assault on Tenaru. But the attack failed miserably. Lacking accurate information on American strength, Ishimoto greatly overestimated his own. Almost all of the troops he led were trapped and killed by the Marines.

If the black man, Vouza, O.B.E., had talked, the results on Guadalcanal might have been different.

Richard Tregaskis

Twenty-eight years old, author of the best seller, Guadalcanal Diary, *Richard Tregaskis has been described as a man of "big appetite, monumental feet and good nature." He's on the large size in build, too: 6 feet 7 inches.*

He was brought up in Elizabeth, N. J. An International News Service reporter at the time of Pearl Harbor, he was assigned first to the U. S. Navy at Hawaii, then, in July, 1942, to the Solomon Islands. It was among our Marines there that he found the material that went into his Diary.

Returning home, he was assigned to the European theater in 1943. In November of that year, while covering the American Fifth Army in Italy, he was severely wounded. Only a speedy and skillful operation saved his life: eleven bone splinters were removed from the right side of his brain. For a time he was partially paralyzed and unable to speak. How-

ever, by the spring of 1945 he had regained his health.

Following Guadalcanal Diary, *Tregaskis published* Invasion Diary, *(1944) which describes the campaign in Sicily and Italy, and a novel,* Stronger Than Fear.

FIGHTING THE WAR WITH FLOWERS

by Pierre J. Huss

During the Nazi occupation of Paris, a bouquet of violets was found each week on the tomb of the Unknown Soldier. Always attached to it was a note reading: "France will live—long after Hitler."

Every week, despite Gestapo vigilance, the little bouquet and note continued to appear—a prophetic symbol that maddened the Nazis with frustration.

I saw the first of these bouquets, with the selfsame message, on June 14, 1940, the day Paris fell. Advance *Panzers* rolled clanking down the deserted Champs Elysées and two Fieseler "Storch" planes landed in the Place de la Concorde and deposited monocled Hitler generals to take over command of Paris.

This was France's blackest hour.

On that day I got my best war story, but not from the parades and speeches of pompous Nazi generals or the spectacle of armed German might rolling along the Parisian boulevards.

On that day our car, which contained several American and other non-Axis war correspondents covering the *Wehrmacht's* blitzkrieg, drove into Paris just behind the first German advance units. We were escorted by Colonel Albrecht Blau, Chief of the High Command's Psychological Intelligence. He led us to the Arc de Triomphe at the identical moment when several high Hitler aides and Army officers arrived to gloat.

They stood and stared in smug self-satisfaction at the little yellow flame that burns continuously before the tomb. Abruptly,

The company was ready to laugh heartily. But Hitler did not laugh.
Disdain and annoyance crossed his face as he flung the bouquet down.

Blau cleared his throat and nudged his adjutant. He had caught sight of the small bouquet of fresh violets, draped with black crepe in token of mourning.

When the adjutant picked up the bouquet and handed it to Blau, the latter found a message tied around the stem. Inscribed with a firm handwriting in blue ink, it read: "France will live—long after Hitler."

Colonel Blau read the note, then hastily shepherded the correspondents back to our cars.

Later that same day, Hitler visited German headquarters in the Hotel Crillon. His gang of henchmen crowded around him where he sat in the reception suite like a Caesar, listening to his yes-men glorify the *Wehrmacht*.

Basking most prominently in the glow of the pleased taskmaster was Otto Abetz, who had been a whole Fifth Column inside France before the war, undermining French stability.

It was Abetz's privilege to repeat to Hitler what he had accomplished. As a climax, Abetz handed Hitler the bouquet and note, smirking as he did so, and said: "This, *mein Führer,* is all that is left of French resistance."

The company stood back, ready to laugh heartily. But Hitler did not laugh. Instead, he read the note as if puzzled. Disdain, then annoyance crossed his face. He threw the bouquet onto the table and said: "Ah, these French! A decadent race! They think in terms of sentimentality instead of hard reality."

Possibly the Fuhrer was annoyed because for a fleeting instant that message touched off a foreboding deep inside his peculiar brain.

Undoubtedly the violets and the note were tossed in the ashcan or crushed under angry German boots. That day, however, marked the beginning of long years of French resistance to the invader. And that resistance did not slacken until the last German had been driven from France.

Pierre J. Huss

Pierre J. Huss is 42 years old. This Luxembourg-born, American-bred newspaperman is an International News Service correspondent of 20 years' standing.

His foreign background, coupled with his knowledge of French and German, won him the post of Central European manager for INS in Berlin. After eight years in that position, he returned to the United States.

With the outbreak of war, Huss was assigned to Washington, D. C., as an authority on Central European affairs. During this period he wrote a book entitled The Foe We Face, picturing Hitler and his new Germany. He served a brief term in the U. S. Army, then was released, became a war correspondent and covered the U. S. campaigns in Africa and the Mediterranean.

At the end of 1943, Huss flew to London to organize INS coverage of the impending invasion of France. From the bridge of the famed British cruiser Scylla, often mentioned in news accounts for its daring actions and yeoman service in convoy duty, he reported the landings of the Allied armies on D-day.

Back in London, Huss joined the illustrious U. S. Third Army, just being formed by General Patton. He was with the Patton forces on their drive into Germany.

The superb fighting quality of U.S. bombers and their crews has often engaged the attention of leading war reporters. This story, and the one that follows—by Merrill Mueller—are typical of the many that praise the stamina of the American Air Forces.

30-TO-1 ON DEATH

by Ernie Pyle

This is the story of a Flying Fortress, "The Thunderbird," and its crew—ten men who wouldn't give up and a plane that wouldn't go down. The incident took place in the winter of '43 when Tripoli was the major supply port for Rommel, and when our fliers from Algeria were helping the British to blast it.

Tripoli was heavily defended by both fighter planes and anti-aircraft guns.

"The Thunderbird" was first hit just as it dropped its bomb load. One engine went out. Then a few minutes later the other engine on the same side went out.

When a four-engined ship loses two engines, both on the same side, it is usually fatal. Therein lies the difference between this feat and other instances of damaged bombers brought home.

"The Thunderbird," badly crippled, was forced to drop below the other Fortresses. And the moment it did, thirty German fighters were on it like vultures. Our Lightning fighters, escorting the Fortresses, stuck by "The Thunderbird" and fought as long as they could, but finally they had to leave her as their fuel ran low. The last fighter left about forty miles from Tripoli. Fortunately, the swarm of German fighters ran out of fuel at the same time.

"The Thunderbird" flew on another twenty miles. Then a single

52

Badly crippled, The Thunderbird *dropped below the other Fortresses. The moment it did, thirty German fighters were on it like vultures.*

German fighter appeared. Its guns damaged the already wounded plane, but they simply couldn't knock the ship out of the air.

Finally, this fighter ran out of ammunition and was forced to leave. Our boys were alone now with their grave troubles. Two engines were gone, most of the guns were out of commission, and they were still more than 400 miles from home. The radio was out. They were losing altitude at a rate of 500 feet a minute.

When they reached 2,000 feet, the pilot consulted his crew. Did they want to jump? No! They would stay with the ship.

The ship was completely out of trim, cocked over at a terrific angle. But they gradually got it trimmed so that it stopped losing altitude. By now they were down to 900 feet—and a solid wall of mountains barred the way homeward.

They flew parallel to the mountains for a long time, but they were now miraculously gaining some altitude. Finally, they got the thing up to 1,500 feet. The lowest pass is 1,600 feet, but they came across at 1,500. Explain that if you can!

The copilot said: "I was blowing on the windshield trying to push her along. Once I almost wanted to reach a foot down and sort of walk us over the pass."

At last they were only forty miles from home. Dusk, coming down on the sandy haze, made the vast, flat desert an indefinite thing, made one oasis look exactly like another.

But they knew when they were near home. Then they shot a red flare and waited for a green flare from our tower. A minute later it came—the most beautiful sight that crew had ever seen. Five more minutes and they never would have made it.

Their weary, crippled plane had flown four and a half hours on one pair of motors. Any pilot will tell you it's impossible.

That night we drank a toast. One man raised his glass to the pilot and said: "Here's to your safe return." But the pilot raised his own glass and proposed instead: "Here's to a damned good airplane." The crew raised their glasses and repeated his toast.

And here is the climax. During that agonizing homeward crawl, this one crippled plane shot down the fantastic total of six German fighters. Officially confirmed!

Ernie Pyle

Ernie Pyle, Boswell for G.I. Joe, was this war's best-loved correspondent. Pyle's column appeared in 366 daily newspapers, 310 weeklies. In 1943 his cables were collected into the book, Here Is Your War, followed in 1944 by Brave Men. Both books are hovering around the million mark in sales.

When the War Department suggested that Hollywood produce a film glorifying America's foot soldier, Lester Cowan sought out Ernie Pyle as the infantry's most articulate interpreter. Though he had come to Ernie only for advice, Cowan decided to make him the model for the figure around whom is woven the story of G.I. Joe.

Born in Indiana 45 years ago, Ernie Pyle served a hitch with the Navy in World War I, later studied at Indiana University.

Newspaper work suited his restless, searching nature, and he put in 12 years on papers in Indiana, Washington, D. C., and New York. By 1935 he was a roving reporter, free to wander where he would. His typical dispatches dealt with unobtrusive, average people.

World War II thrust him into the full floodlight of public attention. In London in 1940 he described the opening of the blitz.

When U. S. troops suddenly appeared in North Africa, Pyle was with them—eating their chow, feeling their emotions, talking their language, braving their dangers. And it was of these things he wrote: the little things, the human and real things.

From North Africa, Pyle accompanied the boys into Italy and France, until physical exhaustion forced him to return to the States.

But ordered rest was irksome; February, 1945, saw him off again, this time with the Navy in the Pacific, where U. S. sailors as well as G.I.'s were the subjects of his inspired reporting.

On the occasion of Pyle's tragic death in April, 1945, President Truman spoke for everyone when he said: "Nobody knows how many individuals in our forces and at home he has helped with his writings. But all Americans understand how wisely, how warmheartedly, how honestly he served his country and profession. He deserves the gratitude of all his countrymen."

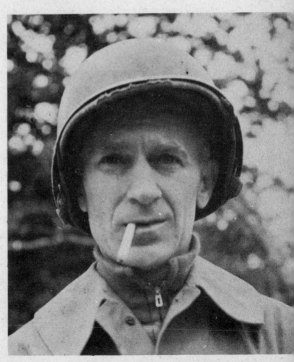

MIRACULOUS MARAUDER

by Merrill ("Red") Mueller

Flying Fortresses aren't the only bombers that can take punishment. Those twin-engined Martin B-26 Marauders can do all right, too.

Consider "Big Butch," one of a Marauder squadron that helped clear the *Luftwaffe* out of Tunisia. On the mission that ended her career, she and her crew both must have had a charm on them.

That day, all Marauder squadrons were ordered out to bomb and strafe enemy airdromes—a strategy employed to keep the Nazi craft on the ground. Bad weather over the targets forced most of the squadrons home again, but "Big Butch" and her wingmates decided on a shipping sweep of the Mediterranean.

As they crossed the enemy-held Tunisian tip, the flight ran into a curtain of flak. When the flight leader's plane was hit, "Big Butch" swung in close to protect that ship in the event of an attack by aircraft. It was then that "Butch" started absorbing punishment. Her crew could feel the hard punches of ack-ack hitting all along her cigar-shaped fuselage. The moment it was possible, the flight ducked into a cloud formation; when "Butch" emerged, she was alone—and in trouble.

She shuddered, hesitated and fell off to one side, but somehow her pilot, Captain James Luttrell (Hanover, N. H.), kept her going. Flak had wrecked the inter-communication telephone system and the radio set, ripped away the right engine cowl, chewed viciously at the right wing. And worse: the left engine was tearing itself to pieces, for a shell had gone clean through it, destroying the cooling

Amid the confusion, "Butch's" nose blew off. The blast of air carried someone's pistol, belt and holster attached, back through the cabin.

system and oil lines.

Captain Luttrell and Lieutenant William Yeager (Cleveland, Ohio), his copilot, managed to kill the left engine before it caught fire, and to feather the prop. And suddenly they found their aileron controls jammed.

Dragging her left engine and with her right wing bucking, "Big Butch" obviously couldn't stay aloft long. As they limped for home, the crew began to lighten the ship by jettisoning their bombs. About half of them were dropped before Luttrell ordered the bomb bays closed.

Then, cutting in the bad engine and racing both until the left one quit cold, burned up, "Butch" got back several hundred feet of altitude. Just as she approached the coast, Bombardier Captain Danny O'Keefe (Brooklyn, N. Y.) and Gunner Staff Sergeant Albert Britton (Taylor, Nebraska) ran to the cockpit to report a 600-ton Axis transport a few miles ahead—and six Messerschmitts up in the sun above her.

The bomb bays were opened again and "Butch" painfully approached the enemy. The Messerschmitts saw the cripple and started downstairs in a hurry. But before they arrived, two of "Butch's" remaining bombs scored direct hits on the ship, which blew up with a terrific roar. Simultaneously, the first Messerschmitt swooped in with machine guns blazing.

Staff Sergeant Marvin Thompson (Washington, D. C.) raked the Nazi from his rear gun turret. But ammunition, stored for the bomber's front guns, had caught fire; now ammo belts were writhing around the cabin and spitting bullets in all directions. Amid the confusion, "Butch's" nose blew off. The blast of air carried someone's pistol, with belt and holster attached, back through the cabin.

At last land was in sight, and American fighters had come from nowhere to engage the remaining Messerschmitts. Captain Luttrell put "Big Butch" into her final glide. As she crossed the enemy lines, Axis gunners cut loose; somehow the Maurauder's crew returned the fire—for which they were later credited. with the destruction of four ack-ack positions.

Luttrell cut the switches and pulled the fire plugs as he approached for a crash landing. At better than 150 miles an hour, "Butch" jolted her belly against the ground, skidded in the dust with a deafening racket and came to a stop—a wreck—in an irrigation ditch. In spite of everything, the whole crew climbed out with only scratches. Then came the pay-off.

A British jeep approached, stopping some distance away. "Big Butch's" crew started to walk toward it. A British officer frantically waved them back.

"Don't move!" he shouted. "You've landed in the middle of a mine field!"

Merrill ("Red") Mueller

This radio and magazine reporter seems to gravitate to danger. Broadcasting from France following the outbreak of war, Mueller left Paris the night before the Germans entered the city, covered the French retreat and surrender.

Pearl Harbor found this young New Yorker aboard a British destroyer, bound for Gibraltar. He went on to Malta, the Middle East and Singapore, where he arrived just before the Japs. He then roamed the South Pacific before moving up to cover the campaigns in North Africa and Sicily.

In 1944, NBC assigned him to General Eisenhower's headquarters and he covered the early invasion of Germany. After a rest in the United States, he returned to the Western Front in March, 1945.

Known as World War II's "most blitzed" correspondent (he went through 700 air raids in London, *72 in Malta, others in North Africa and Europe), Mueller has been decorated three times. He wears the Purple Heart for wounds received in the course of duty.*

"BLESSED EVENT" IN THE PACIFIC

by E. K. Green

"B lessed Event" was a Liberator, and the climax to its career came
when the Pacific stronghold, Rabaul, was still in enemy hands.
Eight of its crew of 10 men were still alive when I talked with
them—but the "Blessed Event" was a shattered wreck.

It was impossible to take Rabaul by surprise. On Bougainville,
which served as an "outpost," enemy eyes watched constantly
for any air movement, flashing a warning to Rabaul as soon as
a formation appeared.

For the "Blessed Event," trouble began when the ship was
almost over Rabaul. No. 3 engine coughed out. At the same time
the other planes in the formation seemed to shoot ahead of the
lame straggler.

"I can't tell you how lonely one feels in those circumstances,"
said Lieutenant Harry P. John, of Crowley, La., the pilot. "The
Japs love stragglers. To see your buddies heading on when you
want them about you most, sure makes you feel bad. But they had
their work to do and couldn't wait for us. The fighter boys couldn't
help either. They were much too busy—with over 100 Zeros in
the sky."

In less than a minute all hell broke loose. Thundering down
out of the sun, their machine guns and cannon belching, came
the Jap Zeros. For 40 minutes the Liberator fought a losing running battle—but she fought. Again and again, 20 mm. and 7.7 mm.
cannon shells exploded within, or hit, her. Half the tail was shot
away. A gaping hole was torn in the waist. The navigator was

Then things became desperate. A sea landing was out of the question with the seriously wounded men aboard, and so was the use of parachutes.

killed with the first shell. Controls were shot away.

Below was the unfriendly Pacific; above, below and on all sides were Zeros spitting fire and death.

"No man ever had a better crew," said Lieutenant John. "Each had a job to do and each was doing it."

As he fought to hold the plane in control after a 20 mm. had ripped and shattered his instrument panel, John felt rather than heard the gasp of his copilot, Raymond Green, of Sayre, Oklahoma, who had been hit in the shoulder and neck.

"Hurt bad, Ray?" John asked. And Ray's cool voice answered: "I'm O.K."

"He's plenty tough, that Ray Green," John said to me later. "Guess it's the Indian in him. He's mighty proud of that."

From nose, turrets, waist and tail, John felt the chatter of his guns. At first there was no time to tally scores, but twice, at least, it seemed that Zeros took mortal wounds.

Now nose gunner Staff Sergeant Bill Barlow, of Redlands, California, felt a thrill of triumph wipe out the pain of a severe skull wound as he caught a Zero and saw it burst into flames. Ball-turret gunner Staff Sergeant John Lemon, of Kent, Ohio, sent a burst into another one and saw it fall.

Every man but three was fighting. In the dead navigator's seat slumped bombardier Lieutenant Lester Kornblow, of New York, his face ashen, bleeding from wounds in the right arm, shoulder and leg. In the waist, radioman Staff Sergeant Tom Craven, of Kalispell, Montana, lay unconscious beside his gun, mortally wounded. By the other waist gun lay Staff Sergeant Dennis Ryan, of Palisade, Minnesota, both collar bones broken and a splinter of shrapnel in his back. He was aiming and firing with one arm.

At the tail gun, Staff Sergeant Joe Dispenza, of Buffalo, New York, had wounds in the hands and face. Staff Sergeant Charles Derrick, of Westminster, South Carolina, came down from the turret seeking aid for a serious abdominal wound, took one look and went back to his guns. Lemon, wounded in the foot, came up from the ball and took over the waist guns. He got another Zero from there. Dispenza got still another.

They were over St. George's Channel now, and things looked desperate. John himself had wounds in the right arm and face but he scarcely realized it. By the time the last Zero turned back, out of ammunition and low on gas, another of the "Blessed Event's" engines failed. It was an emergency field landing—or else.

A sea landing was out of the question with the seriously wounded men aboard; so was the use of parachutes. The radio had been out of action since the start. One rudder was shot away and all systems were gone—electric, automatic, oxygen.

And now another hazard—under manual control, only one wheel went down and it stuck. The odds against the crew were 1000 to one. The two functioning engines faltered and Lieutenant John dropped the tail hurriedly. The big craft touched . . . struck . . . splintered . . . and slipped 200 yards in a perfect belly landing.

The crew had lost two men—Craven died that night—but the "Blessed Event" had accounted for four Zeros certainly shot down, and six "probables," out of 100 that had taken the sky.

E. K. Green

E. K. Green is a war correspondent in the South Pacific for Overseas Press, a news association serving British and American papers. He also acts as war correspondent for The Auckland (New Zealand) Star.

Though Green, a native of New Zealand, is only 36 years old, he has been in newspaper work as a reporter and as a special writer for seventeen years and he has twice been a winner of the New Zealand Journalist Prize, an award similar to the Pulitzer prize in the United States.

Green's articles have appeared in leading periodicals of Canada and the United States.

LOVE IN A JAP PRISON

by Wenzell Brown

When war struck Hong Kong in December, 1941, Kate Malley and Virgil Bancroft were caught—as I was—without warning. She was a nurse, Irish, big, not young—a warm, laughing woman. Her large, capable hands were miracles of tenderness.

Virgil Bancroft was an American, a professor at the university in Hong Kong. He was small and frail, a lover of jade and poetry.

Jap bombs threw them together. As Hong Kong tried to resist the invader, Mrs. Malley sprang to action behind the lines. Sometimes she rode out to the front in the trucks to help bring the wounded back to the makeshift hospital in the Hong Kong Hotel. Through nightmarish days and nights she tended those wounded, her ministrations deft, her cheerful smile unfaltering. And Professor Bancroft helped her, shyly, fumbling, but eager to do his bit.

Then, on Christmas Day, the city surrendered. Soon all civilians were rounded up and crowded into dirty little hotels. Eventually, after days without food, or light or sleep, they were paraded through the streets to Stanley Prison grounds, where they were interned.

It was there we learned to know Kate Malley—and to love her. For her courage and tenderness were unshakable. Soon men, women and children alike were looking to her for comfort, reassurance. And she never failed.

Virgil Bancroft was stricken with dysentery; she nursed him through. There were no beds available in the prison camp but Mrs. Malley contrived a bed for the professor from pine boughs

In her worn and tattered pink dress, Kate Malley stood beside Professor
Bancroft. Never, I think, have the words "I do" sounded more stirring.

and canvas spread on the concrete floor. She gave to him freely from the tiny store of food and medicine that she had managed to bring with her to the camp.

Months passed, and hunger and hardship laid many another low; she devised remedies out of nothing, rallied the able-bodied, watched over the children, solaced the dying. To ward off scurvy, she brewed us vile concoctions of pine needles. To avert calcium deficiency, she made us swallow pulverized bone. But she forgot one person: herself.

Before long her own teeth became as brittle as chalk, her legs swollen with beriberi. Her hair started to fall out in clumps. Her pink linen dress, the only one the Japs let her bring, grew tattered. The dress she patched as well as she could, and when her shoes wore out, she stuffed them with paper.

Yet each day, her ministrations done, she and the professor sat together by the prison gate, talking. It was clear to see that Virgil Bancroft, who had loved jade and the classics of Old China, found in Kate Malley a beauty that neither suffering, disfigurement nor the sordidness of the camp could destroy.

Then through our apathetic ranks flashed an electric word: repatriation! A ship was coming. Freedom! Little knots of excited men and women gathered to scan the horizon; check again and again the sweet fact of deliverance.

But not for all of us. Only the Americans were to go. The British must stay. For Virgil Bancroft — deliverance. For Kate Malley—nothing.

The little professor tried his desperate best. While others chattered of coming departure, he sought out the officials in charge, pleading, cajoling—in vain.

Mrs. Malley was, unarguably, British. And no British were to be exchanged. Not even marriage to an American could effect her release.

Days passed. Delays were endless. Nerves grew taut as the prospect of release became certain. Small personal possessions were passed on. Messages and addresses were memorized for delivery to friends and relatives. And through it all Kate Malley continued to care for the sick; Virgil Bancroft, more wraithlike than ever, was in constant attendance on her, his drawn face betraying the agony of his spirit.

And then the little professor made his decision. Early one morning, while the dawn sun turned the sky to flaming crimson and shimmering gold, a few of us gathered on the great rock that overlooks the bay. The missionary was on hand, and Virgil Bancroft with him. Then, up the path, still in her tattered pink linen dress, Kate Malley came to stand beside the professor.

There they were married. Never, I think, have the simple words "I do" sounded more stirring. And when the *Gripsholm* sailed off to America, there they remained. God knows their final fate. But *I* know the happiness they found brought renewed faith to every soul still waiting deliverance from Stanley Prison.

Wenzell Brown

Wenzell Brown's first job was on the Evening News *of Portland, Maine, his home town. He was graduated from Rollins College, received his master's degree from Columbia, and in 1940 became a teacher at Lingnan University in China.*

When Hong Kong fell to the Japs, he was taken prisoner and interned for seven months in Stanley Prison. He was returned to the United States through an exchange of civilian prisoners on the Gripsholm.

In his book, Hong Kong Aftermath, *Brown tells of the prison and its 2,700 starving civilians. During his term of imprisonment his weight fell from 200 to 102 pounds.*

He is the author of many articles in leading magazines and has written a second book of non-fiction, Revolution on Our Doorstep.

FLIGHT FROM FEAR

by Otto Gelsted

The faint splash of oars broke the silence of the Danish night. When the moon peeped from behind a cloud, I could see faint shadows gliding across the water—dinghies plying back and forth between the shore and an invisible goal out on the limitless sea. The small boats, their oars swathed in cloth to deaden the sound, were packed with refugees—women, children, old people and a few sabotage experts who were wanted by the Gestapo.

It was midnight when we reached our destination, a fishing boat lying at anchor far off the Copenhagen shore. Its decks, cabin and hold were already crowded with human beings who had been brought out in earlier boat loads. Those on deck helped pull the sick and feeble from the dinghies.

"We have a blind man here," cried a voice from one of the boats. "Give us a hand." From another boat a stretcher was hoisted on board, bearing a pregnant woman who had been given drugs so that her baby would not be born during the crossing.

Suddenly the stillness was shattered by the starting of the engine, which coughed and stuttered so loudly that we felt certain the patrols on shore would hear it. Then came the penetrating chime of the engine-room bell; it was as if all Denmark's church bells were ringing farewell to us.

As the ship slowly made its way eastward, toward Sweden and freedom, I leaned against the railing and looked back toward Denmark, where the moon shone above the autumn woods. Once we had made love beneath that moon and listened to the call of

Every gleam of light caused fear in us. Was it friend or enemy? The panting of the engine was terrifying against the silence of the sea.

the cuckoo in the Zealand woods, but now it was like a hostile searchlight revealing us to the German patrols. It seemed incredible that this dark, menacing sea was really Ore Sund, the peaceful sound where — on faraway summer days before the war — suntanned girls, white yachts and multicolored canoes played like dolphins in the blue water.

Every gleam of light caused fear among us, for who knew whether it was friend or enemy? To the south, a lightship flashed its signals and searchlights threw their pale beams across the sky like ghostly fingers touching and crossing in the dark. The panting of the engine was a terrifying noise against the silence of the sea.

There was no food aboard the refugee ship, only a keg of water. Many among us had not slept the night before, and had spent the day hidden in sheds or cellars along the coast. For most of us this voyage meant that our own little world had been shattered, and none knew when it would be rebuilt.

An old woman next to me whispered, almost inaudibly: "I took some pills when the Gestapo came to the door. It was really the pills that saved me. I was unconscious when the German agents entered and the neighbors persuaded them that I was dying."

Her voice became strong as she added: "If they should discover this boat, I'll drown myself. They'll never get their hands on me!"

The moon disappeared as the haze became thicker. A few lights gleamed faintly from the direction of Sweden. Suddenly the boat shuddered to a stop and the pounding of the engine grew in violence.

"We're on a bank," the skipper said. "We must have missed the buoy in the darkness."

I could read fear in the faces around me as the engine struggled and coughed, then relief as the boat shook and began to move again. Cautiously she edged forward, as if groping in a pitch-dark corridor. But a few minutes after we reached open water, our hearts were filled with fear again. The ship slowed down and suddenly stopped dead.

A voice from the engine room shouted: "One of the pistons has broken."

70

"Can't you fix it?" the skipper asked, alarm in his voice.

"Not until we reach Sweden."

Just then we saw a light approaching and heard the rhythmical beat of another engine. We were paralyzed with terror when a searchlight was suddenly flashed on us. It played questioningly the length of the ship.

The other boat was a patrol craft. We could make out its dim outlines behind the searchlight. But was it German or Swedish? Were we yet within Swedish territorial waters? And if we were, would a German patrol boat seize us anyway? We could scarcely breathe; our chests were too constricted.

A gruff voice challenged us: "Where do you hail from?"

"Denmark."

We saw a man step into the searchlight's glow and stretch out his arms as if to embrace our entire ship.

"*Välkommen!*" he shouted heartily.

"Welcome to Sweden!"

Otto Gelsted

Otto Gelsted, author, free-lance journalist, theater critic, native of Denmark, is known to his countrymen as a man of liberal and democratic thought. Gelsted's books, published in Denmark, bear the titles: Toward Clarity *(1931),* During the Tempest *(1934), and* Selected Poems *(1938).*

He was always defiantly anti-Nazi, and when the Germans seized his country, he was forced to go into hiding until he could escape to Sweden. He tells of that escape in this story.

While in Sweden, Gelsted has had time to write his recently published novel, The Jews of Husaby.

CITED—FOR A HANGOVER

by William W. Boddie

There is a cryptic—and amusing—tale that comes from the Pacific, and it has already become legendary. No editor or correspondent can get any confirmation of it from authoritative sources, but one can get a smile that might mean anything.

The story goes that at a certain naval headquarters the commanding admiral was concerned about loose talk, so he asked the Office of Naval Intelligence to see what it could do to tighten up on security. Naval Intelligence took over and sent operatives to such obvious places as the messes and the bars around town.

One place that the admiral may not have thought would be tested was his own headquarters offices. But they were.

One morning a Naval Intelligence officer, wearing no insignia of rank, entered the admiral's headquarters without challenge from the sentries.

Everyone apparently assumed he had a perfect right to be there. Taking full advantage of the situation, he ranged freely through the building, from one office to the next.

He took confidential publications and secret charts, even openly copied ship positions from a map which, the legend asserts, was in the admiral's own office. No one stopped him. No one showed even the slightest interest in what he was doing.

As the operative was passing through one of the halls, he saw the code room. This is the most secret place on any ship or naval installation, and only specially authorized personnel are ever permitted to enter.

The officer stealthily walked toward the desk, intending to rifle its drawers. Inadvertently he kicked a wastepaper basket, sent it clattering over the floor.

Looking through the door of this code room, the intelligence officer saw a young ensign who was resting his head on a desk. He seemed to be asleep. Actually, the ensign was suffering the mortifications of an extreme hangover. He had been high the previous night, and now he was very low.

He was softly slobbering out repentance. For in addition to his head, he had had a bawling-out from his chief for coming in late that day. He felt mean and vicious.

. The intelligence officer stealthily entered the room and walked toward a near-by desk, intending to rifle its drawers. Inadvertently, he kicked a wastepaper basket, sending it clattering across the floor. The overhung ensign, his nerves tortured beyond endurance, sprang to his feet and drew his pistol.

"What the hell are you doing here?" he screamed. "Speak up before I blow your guts out!"

The legend continues that the admiral received a stinging memorandum on the state of security in his own headquarters. Only one officer was cited for diligent attention to duty. That was the ensign with the hangover.

William W. Boddie

William W. Boddie, a South Carolinian, was educated at the College of Charleston and the University of North Carolina.

He joined the staff of Newsweek *in 1940, and until December, 1941, was assigned to* Newsweek's *Defense Department. With the outbreak of war, he covered the War and Navy Departments in Washington.*

He was Newsweek's *war correspondent from April to November, 1943, reporting the Rendova and New Georgia Island actions and the Marcus Island attack from a carrier. Recurrent malaria forced his return, and he is now on the magazine's staff in New York.*

HANDSHAKE WITH DEATH

by Larry Lesueur

It was a warm October night during the London blitz. The Nazis were overhead, dumping their high explosives on the bomb-groggy city. A group of correspondents were standing about watching a heavy antiaircraft battery on one of the hills of a London park.

British antiaircraft gunners, stripped to the waist, gleaming with sweat, rammed home shining shells. Officers barked orders and men pivoted the long guns to follow the enemy planes across the sky, crisscrossed with searchlights.

All around the park, houses were afire, silhouetting the blacked-out skyline against a lurid red glow. High overhead, the shells burst in yellow blossoms of hot metal.

The correspondents groveled as the gross shriek of a bomb ended in an earthquaking explosion. A slender plume of black smoke hung over a little frame building a quarter of a mile away, the scene illuminated by near-by conflagrations.

"I'm afraid they got Battery Headquarters, sir," said a young British lieutenant with a clipped mustache.

"Go down and see what you can salvage before the fire gets too bad," his imperturbable colonel ordered.

The lieutenant trotted back in five minutes, bearing a bottle of Scotch whisky and two enameled cups.

"This is all that's left of Headquarters, sir," he reported.

Some correspondents tilted the chipped cups. Others, less fastidious, drank from the bottle. The tight feeling in their chests gradually relaxed.

"Don't touch it!" the colonel shouted hastily. But he was too late. The

war correspondent had already slashed one of the heavy parachute cords.

Suddenly, in the glare of searchlights and fires, someone sighted a parachute falling fast. As a single voice, the gunners cried, "We got one!"

"Fix bayonets and bring in that parachutist," the colonel ordered. A gun crew ceased firing and disappeared into the night, rifles at the ready. They returned faster than they had gone out.

"That wasn't no flier, sir," said a breathless cockney sergeant. "That was a parachute bomb!"

The colonel quickly translated thought into action. "Down, everybody!" he shouted, flinging himself to the ground. The correspondents were already flat on their faces.

Minutes passed. Finally the colonel arose cautiously. "A dud, I guess," he said sheepishly.

There was a lull in the bombing just then and the correspondents decided to examine the mystery bomb.

It lay near by, on the soft ground of a plowed field. It was huge—eight feet long and four around, painted black, with shiny brass fuses. Beyond it sprawled a 20-foot, green silk parachute. One correspondent, flicking his flashlight over the ominous smoothness of the bomb, decided to cut off one of the heavy shroud cords of the 'chute, as a souvenir.

"Don't touch it!" the colonel shouted hastily. But he was too late. The correspondent had already slashed, and he gleefully held up the severed parachute cord.

Soon the fires began to dim and the angry flush of the skyline was replaced by the gray of dawn. The correspondents had seen enough. The car taking them back to their hotels was a safe mile away from the gun site when the land mine exploded. The blast shook the car, and windows were shattered for miles around.

Next time we saw the impetuous souvenir hunter, he said, "I've got that parachute cord in a place where I'll never forget it. It's holding up my pajamas."

Larry Lesueur

Larry Lesueur is the third in his family to take up journalism; his grandfather was the publisher of two newspapers in Iowa; his father was formerly a correspondent for the New York Tribune.

Lesueur graduated from New York University in 1931 and put in six years with the United Press before joining the staff of the Columbia Broadcasting System in 1939. His first assignment with CBS was to report the activities of the R.A.F. and the British Army in France during the early days of the war.

When France fell, he made his way to England where he joined the network's London staff. There he broadcast descriptions of the work of the R.A.F. and intimate accounts of everyday life and people in war-wracked England.

Lesueur gained a wide reputation for his sense of humor and imperturbable acceptance of the hazards of war. On one occasion, while he was dining with friends in London, a sudden German raid seemed to center on the hotel in which they sat. Chandeliers began to fall and plaster dust filled the air. Guests and waiters alike hurried to the nearest shelter—but Lesueur remained behind. Undisturbed, he finished his meal. Then, discovering that the waiters were not yet functioning, he walked into the kitchen and helped himself to dessert.

In the autumn of 1941 he was assigned as CBS' Moscow correspondent, serving for a time at Kuibyshev, the temporary capital, until the siege of Moscow was lifted.

When he returned to the States in October, 1941, he had traveled extensively in Russia, had studied its people and learned much of Russian character. His book, Twelve Months That Shook the World, tells of those travels and of his observations.

In June, 1943, CBS sent him to London again, and he covered 1944's D-day and the subsequent bloody action on the Western Front.

REQUIEM FOR A HERO

by S/Sgt. Alvin M. Josephy

This is the story of how Navy Pharmacist's Mate Virgil Warren, of Oakland, California, came to sing *God Bless America*—not very well, he admits—on a hot beachhead at Guam.

It happened during the fiercest fighting there. Marine Master Gunnery Sergeant Israel Margolis, of Los Angeles, had been hit trying to man a machine gun. No one knows how he got there. The master gunnery sergeant was an expert in charge of the maintenance and repair of his outfit's weapons. A man with that job usually is to be found somewhere in the rear.

But Margolis must have seen the wounded streaming back. He knew what was going on. All of a sudden, he was on top of a 100-foot cliff where men were fighting and dying. And he was looking for action.

Margolis was 48 years old, not young for a front-line fighter. But, like many Marines, he was a professional. Born in Volkovisk, Russia, he had fought as an officer of the Czar in the last war. After the Russian Revolution, he had joined the American Army in France, then had come to the United States, been naturalized and joined the Marine Corps.

Israel Margolis was short and wiry, with a square-cut head. He had been all over with the Marine Corps. His record book showed service in the Caribbean, China, New Zealand and the Solomon Islands. He was in action on Bougainville before coming to Guam.

The Japs had that cliff top on Guam well marked. It was flat and open. The Marines were trying to bring together enough

80

He sobbed. Muddy Marines, shaken by battle, crowded around. One, then others, knelt. Warren tried again. "Stand beside her and guide her . . ."

strength there to launch an attack. Machine guns were holding them up, sweeping the level with murderous fire.

Just after Margolis was first seen there, Jap machine gunners spotted one of our guns. In succession, five Marines tried to man that gun and each was hit. The fifth, though wounded, tried to drag the gun to a new position.

Master Gunnery Sergeant Margolis went to his aid. Pulling the gun away, he began to man it himself. The Japs caught him immediately. Bullets crashed into his legs and hips, and he fell sideways.

Pharmacist's Mate Warren pulled him to the edge of the cliff, but there was no way to get him down. The corpsman dressed his wounds. It was useless. Margolis was dying, and knew it. He lay in the open, within sight and sound of the fighting, and pleaded with the corpsman to leave him and help the others.

Warren looked around helplessly. If there were only a block and tackle, some sling arrangement to lower the wounded man down the 100-foot cliff. But men were just beginning to fashion a sling. Margolis' life wouldn't wait.

Final thoughts must have crowded the man's mind as he lay there—the St. Petersburg cadet school, the Czar's Uhlans, the AEF, the Marine Corps and eighteen years of service, his adopted land that he would never see again. . . .

Suddenly, he opened his eyes. Warren asked him if he wanted anything. Margolis stared hard a moment, then nodded. Warren knelt beside him.

"Please," Margolis whispered, "please sing *God Bless America.*"

The corpsman swallowed. He tried. *"God bless America, land that I love . . ."*

He sobbed. Muddy Marines, shaken by battle, crowded around. Warren tried again. *"Stand beside her and guide her . . ."* Lumps came to the throats of the Marines. One, then others, knelt. *"Through the night with the light from above . . ."*

Margolis' eyelids fluttered.

"From the mountains and the prairies . . ." On the clifftop above the beachhead at Guam there was a hush. *"From the oceans white*

with foam." Now the corpsman lifted his voice and the notes came full:

"God bless America, my home, sweet home." *

In the silence that followed, the tough little soldier, United States Marine and naturalized American, died.

S/Sgt. Alvin M. Josephy

At the end of his sophomore year at Harvard, Marine Staff Sergeant Alvin M. Josephy, Jr., sold an original story to Metro-Goldwyn-Mayer and went to Hollywood to write the movie script.

Later, he became a staff correspondent in Mexico for the New York Herald Tribune, and next worked for radio station WOR as assistant director of news and special events.

In March, 1942, Josephy joined a Government radio bureau which was later incorporated into the Office of War Information.

The following year he enlisted in the Marine Corps and was sent to the Pacific. Appointed a combat correspondent, he participated in the Solomons campaign, the assault on Guam and the furious action at Iwo Jima.

At Guam, carrying a hand microphone, he recorded the first eyewitness description of a ship-to-shore amphibious operation. With the first outfit to wade ashore—across a 450-yard reef under fire—he had his mobile recording equipment stowed in a halftrack and he walked alongside. His description, electrically transcribed, has been played over *the major radio networks.*

He has made combat records, to be broadcast later, from a front-line foxhole at night, from an ambush in the jungle and from swamps during mopping-up operations.

Early in 1945, he was ordered to Washington to write a book, with other combat correspondents, on the Iwo Jima action.

Josephy has been awarded the Bronze Star for "heroic achievement."

HOW A MARINE KILLED HIS PAL

by Stefan Heym

Sergeant Lebedeff was one of four Marines, veterans of Guadal-canal, attached to our outfit "for purposes of special training," their orders said. The captain didn't approve of them. Underneath his overbearing attitude was the resentment often found in the typical garrison soldier against the man who has been "out there" and knows about the real thing. The four Marines forced the captain to be continually on the defensive, and though they never made a slighting remark, I believe he was secretly afraid of their smiles.

Especially Lebedeff's smile. The sergeant wasn't talkative and he kept much to himself. He was barely Marine height, slight, freckled and almost beardless. Once, the captain was heard to say to his lieutenant: "And *that* they call a leatherneck!"

Soon the captain started a little war of his own against Lebedeff. The climax came one night during maneuvers.

By then, most of us were grimy and tired. Sham fighting had become a boring routine, a game for no stakes.

This night Lebedeff and three of us were sent on patrol. The captain gave us our instructions: "The password for tonight is 'Sweet Home.' Don't any of you forget it. Anyone approaching this post will be stopped and challenged. He will be let through only on rendering the correct password. Is that clear, Sergeant Lebedeff?"

"Yes, sir," the sergeant said quietly.

What was all the shouting about, anyway, we wondered. This

"Why don't you challenge us?" Lebedeff demanded. "Aw, go on," said the guard. "Cut the kid stuff." Lebedeff's face grew stern. "Challenge me!"

emphasis on passwords seemed ridiculous. After all, we knew most of the men by face or name. They knew us.

The guard must have thought the same. When we came back from our patrol, he nodded and grinned at us.

But Lebedeff stopped. "Why don't you challenge us?"

"Aw, go on," said the guard. "Cut the kid stuff."

Lebedeff's face darkened. "Challenge me!" he shouted.

The guard, taken aback, obeyed. "Password," he demanded.

"Sweet," the sergeant replied. "Countersign?"

"Home," the guard answered.

The loud exchange had aroused the command tent. The flaps were thrown open and the captain came toward us.

"Do you want the enemy to hear?" he reprimanded. Then he recognized Lebedeff and snapped: "What's all the noise about?"

Sergeant Lebedeff said nothing.

"It was about the password . . ." offered the guard.

"What's that?" The captain turned to Lebedeff. "Sergeant, I told you there would be no laxity on passwords . . . ."

Lebedeff broke in, his voice thick.

"I'm touchy on the subject of passwords myself, sir," he said. "I had to kill a man for not giving one, and he was a friend."

The captain coughed, surprised. There followed an odd silence.

Then Lebedeff said, "Judd Aubrey—" and he spoke the name as if he were holding the dead man's hand—"Judd Aubrey was the laughing kind. To him this war was what I guess his whole life had been. A big unending joke. Judd laughed at everything —the mosquitoes, the rations, the Jap snipers. He went through the jungle as if it did not concern him and could not touch him."

"Speak to the point!" said the captain.

Lebedeff continued:

"But Aubrey's great joke was passwords. He would distort them, twist them, sometimes not give them at all, or steal up behind and suddenly jump out to shout them in the guard's ear. It was bad. It infected the other men, and many stopped taking the passwords seriously. Finally the colonel put a stop to it. Quite simply. He issued orders that whoever did not give the password

86

"Then I shot like mad. I emptied the whole magazine. It was difficult to see where I was hitting but I wanted to kill Aubrey good and dead."

87

or gave it incorrectly, was to be shot.

"Aubrey griped some because he had been deprived of his fun, but he saw the colonel's point.

"I was standing guard one night when Judd Aubrey and two other men went out on patrol. I'll never forget that evening. It must have been still bright above the treetops but, down in the jungle where we lived, the half light was a shadowy thickness one could almost cut with a machete. After a time, your ears grow accustomed to natural noises—the sound of wind, plants and animals. You scarcely hear them. Instead, you wait for the hardly noticeable cracking of dead wood, the sucking sound of the marshy ground, which indicates the approach of man—whether friend or enemy.

"And then it came. A firmer shadow seemed to loosen itself from the rest. Slowly I trained my rifle on it and said, not too loudly, 'Halt!'

"It was not quite time for Aubrey's return. Yet it seemed to me that I recognized him—the white teeth glistening between his laughing lips, the way he swung his arm. And the others appeared to be right behind him—if I could trust my eyes.

" 'Halt!' I said again.

"The shadow kept creeping up. I cursed Aubrey and his jokes. Why wouldn't he learn that this war was no funny game? It was being played for keeps.

" 'Aubrey!' I cried in desperation. 'Aubrey, halt! The password! You know I'll have to shoot you!'

"I strained my ears. I though he might whisper the word for fear lurking Japs might overhear it—and I felt sure he was too good a soldier to ignore the colonel's recent strict command or doubt that I could do anything but obey it. But not even a whispered password came to my ears, only the heavy breathing of the jungle and the faint, steady, creeping approach of the shadow or shadows.

"I shouted once more. I don't know what.

"Then I fired. I shot like mad. I emptied the whole magazine of eight rounds. I wanted to kill Aubrey good and dead. It was difficult to see where I was hitting, and I didn't want him to suffer.

"My shots alarmed the camp. Men came running. I explained as fast as I could, hating every word for the precious seconds they cost. But the men couldn't just go out and look; you never could tell who was around on Guadalcanal. The search had to be organized and the searchers had to keep their fingers on their triggers.

"Then we found Judd Aubrey. He was dead. I had hit him clean through the head, thank God.

"We also found three Japs, one dead, two badly wounded.

"They must have used Judd Aubrey as a shield, for he carried no weapons when we picked up his body, and we never heard of the two other men on that patrol with him. The Japs had wanted him to lead them into our positions.

"Judd had known the password all right, but he kept it to himself. Probably thought it was a good joke he was pulling on the Japs, probably laughed—but laughed to himself. . . ."

"What was the password?" asked the captain.

"Sweet home," said the sergeant.

Stefan Heym

Stefan Heym, a German, was beaten by the Nazis for writing an anti-Nazi poem while he was a student at the University of Berlin. In 1933, he was forced to flee Germany to escape the Gestapo.

In Prague, he earned his living by writing for periodicals and the theater. Later, he got his master's degree at the University of Chicago as an exchange student.

Heym's first novel, Hostages, *written in English and published in 1942, won high critical regard. He was inducted into the U. S. Army in 1943. His second novel,* Of Smiling Peace, *was finished just before the Allied invasion of Normandy.*

CHRISTMAS EVE IN MADRID

by Donald Grant

We were sitting in a wadi near Fondouk Pass one night. A man who joined Major Mark Martin and me there was introduced simply as Pierre, a French officer who had fled Occupied Europe to fight with the Allies in Africa. I never learned his full name, but this is the story he told against a background of rumbling artillery fire as the battle for the Pass continued.

That day we had seen men die and men who wished they were dead. In the midst of the cruelty and suffering of war, Pierre spoke of the power of the gentle Jesus Christ, who lived on earth not so far from the spot where we were sitting.

"Two of us decided to escape Occupied France together," began Pierre, drawing on his cigarette until the glow of it etched his ruggedly handsome face in red outline against the black of the night.

"We had arranged for underground agents in Spain to meet us just over the border in the mountains. They were to be dressed as Spanish Border Patrol Police—but, as luck would have it, the real Border Patrol happened along just as we crawled across, and my friend was captured.

"He shouted a warning and I ran just in time. For three days I hid in the mountains, eating dried berries which I dug out of the snow. Then I made my way to Madrid.

"By the time I got there I was pretty well worn out. My clothes were torn and I was cold and hungry. I had no friends there and no money. I knew that if I were picked up by the police I should

The Christmas bells pealed out in redoubled force. I held my breath
waiting for the answer. It came slowly and softly, after a long pause.

be turned over to the Gestapo.

"Dragging myself through the streets I picked up a discarded newspaper and noticed the date. It was December 24, 1942—the day before Christmas. Under the twin spurs of hunger and fatigue my brain was working furiously.

"I knew of a very ambitious and wealthy Spaniard who had been a notorious pro-Fascist, but who was reputed to be a devout Christian also. In the desperation of the moment I decided to find out whether on Christmas Eve the Spaniard would be ruled by his politics—or by his religion.

"I walked to his home and threw myself on his mercy in the name of Christ. The Spaniard gave me a long look, finally invited me in, fed me and gave me a bed. It was a cheap act of mercy if he were to turn me over to the police later, but I was too exhausted to care. I lay down and did not awaken until the bells were ringing for midnight Mass."

The French officer paused a while and the three of us sat listening to the distant booming of cannon.

"Just outside my door, as I awoke, a Spanish policeman was talking to my host. 'But, señor,' said a rasping voice that sent shivers down my spine, 'we were told that the stranger entered your house this evening. He is a French DeGaullist—and he is wanted by the German authorities.'

"I held my breath, waiting for the answer. It came after a long pause, during which the Christmas bells pealed out in redoubled force, filling the air with their silver music. 'I am sorry, Señor Policeman,' said my host, speaking slowly and softly, 'but you are mistaken.'

"His tone was final. I heard him walk out of the house with the policeman. Both of them were going to attend the Christmas Mass. . . ."

Neither Major Martin nor I spoke when Pierre had finished. Even the far-off rumble of artillery had ceased for the moment. The stars in our African sky seemed very bright.

Donald Grant

Donald Grant began his journalistic career as a reporter for the Des Moines Register and Tribune. In 1941, the quality of his work won him a Nieman Fellowship at Harvard. While studying there, he collaborated with other Nieman Fellows on a book, Newsman's Holiday.

In May, 1942, this Minnesota-born reporter joined the staff of LOOK, was assigned to its Washington bureau. After seven months there, he went abroad for LOOK as war correspondent.

From England, he flew with Flying Fortresses over Germany, sailed with British gunboats in night raids on the German-held coast. In Africa he went into combat with infantrymen and tank crews during the Tunisian campaign. He was the first correspondent to go inside Greece with the guerrilla fighters.

After returning to this country for a brief period, Grant set out again, this time to cover the European invasion with General Patton.

He is back in the United States again, and is now on the staff of the Post-Dispatch in St. Louis.

93

HISTORY OUTSIDE MESSINA

by John Daly

One sunny morning in August, 1943, Don Whitehead, of the AP, and I lay quietly in a sewage ditch outside Messina, Sicily, reflecting on the accuracy of German long-range artillery fire. As we gazed up, wondering if the barrage was over, a jeep pulled up and a Texas voice drawled:

"Why don't you two white wings get out of that sewer and come with me? We're going to make history."

It was Lieutenant Bill Dougherty, of Dallas, speaking. He was commander of a battery of Long Toms—the huge 155 mm. guns, which it seems so strange to call rifles.

"Come on," said Dougherty, "we're going to fire the first shell into *Festung Europa*—the first American shell to be fired into Europe proper."

Europe proper, meaning Italy, lay less than 15 miles beyond the Strait and City of Messina. Dougherty was getting one of his guns set to fire across the strait. Whitehead and I watched impatiently as a bulldozer knocked down walls and trees, shunted the gun into position. Then the gun crew began the tedious job of digging in, calibrating and lining up.

Dougherty patted the side of the Long Tom—it was called "Draftee"—and said, "I've been waiting a long time for this. I'm gonna pull the lanyard myself."

Everybody was getting a little excited about this business of firing the first shell.

Alben Keel, "Pfc., Atoka, Tennessee, suh," who had pulled

Only minutes afterward, a jeep bounced into the clearing and, before it had jerked to a stop, out jumped Lieutenant General Omar Bradley.

the lanyard through North Africa and Sicily, on this historic occasion had yielded to the lieutenant.

To take some of the sting out of his disappointment, Keel carefully prepared the shell, then took a pencil out of his pocket and wrote on the metal casing, "To Hitler, with love from Al." A more traveled comrade-in-arms sent compliments from himself, his wife —and his girl friend.

The emplacing was nearly finished, and as Dougherty announced that we would be ready to fire in about five minutes, a car drove in from the road. Out stepped Colonel Walter W. Hess, Jr., commanding officer of the regiment.

The colonel coughed and said, "I've had this regiment, you know, for four and a half years, and I have looked forward to just one thing. I'm an old man and have few pleasures, but if I could pull the lanyard on the first American shell to land in Italy, it would make this one of the happiest days of my life. Do you suppose I could do so without disappointing anyone too much?"

Dougherty laughed wryly and said, "I was going to do it, sir. But we'd be honored if you'd take over. I don't know of anyone who has a better right."

Colonel Hess took a 30-second refresher course in lanyard pulling from Private Keel. Then "Draftee" bellowed triumphantly, flame shot out of its mouth, and 100 pounds of steel whispered off into space—destination: San Giovanni, Italy.

Only minutes afterward, a jeep bounced into the clearing and out jumped Lieutenant General Omar Bradley, commander of the American Second Corps.

He looked at "Draftee," out of which a steady stream of shells was roaring toward Italy, and his face fell.

"Well," he sighed, "I see somebody beat me to it. I hoped I'd be able to pull the lanyard on the first gun to fire into Hitler's Europe."

"Draftee" bellowed again. The colonel said he was sorry. The general smiled, the lieutenant smiled. Private Keel smiled. Everyone was quite content. It didn't really matter, now, who had pulled the lanyard.

John Daly

John Daly received his education in the United States, though he lived in Johannesburg, South Africa, until he was nine years old.

In 1937, Daly joined the staff of radio station WTOP in Washington and covered special events such as presidential campaign trips and political conventions.

He arrived in London in February, 1943, as a reporter for the Columbia Broadcasting Company.

Says Mr. Daly: "I went to Africa in late June, 1943, and from then on followed the campaigns, specifically, of the American Third and 45th Divisions, going with them through the Sicilian campaign and into Italy. Other units I covered in the Sicilian and Italian fighting were the U. S. First and Ninth Divisions—part of the Sicilian invasion force—and the 34th and 36th Divisions, which bore a major share of the Italian fighting.

"My closest escape from death came on Thanksgiving Day of 1943 at the little oasis town of Bou Sada in North Africa's Sahara Desert. A member of the French Spahi Garrison loaned me his Arabian steed.

I dashed off across the desert in the best Hollywood manner, the horse tripped in a wadi, I lost both stirrups and damn near wound up nurturing daisies in the Sahara sand—if daisies only grew there."

Since his return to the U. S. in the spring of 1944, Daly has been the narrator of the CBS feature, Report to the Nation, as well as a regular network news reporter.

WAR STORY FROM OCCUPIED FRANCE

by T/3 Jack Denton Scott

They were the strangest looking G.I.'s I have ever seen. Dressed in private's uniforms, with gay red epaulets on their shoulders and dark blue hats cocked on the backs of their heads, the three sat close together on a bunk talking softly. The pot-bellied stove in the center of the barracks threw off terrific heat. One of them got up and fiddled with the damper for a moment. The red belly of the stove began to lose its color.

Through their poor English and my very bad French I discovered that they were members of the French Air Force, that they had escaped from France and had just spent several months in the United States learning radio. Now they were Europe-bound with a boatload of American soldiers, on their way back to the war zone to fly combat.

The red epaulets signified that they were sergeants—the equivalent of our staff sergeants. Before they had left the radio technical school, they had all voluntarily signed agreements that, if they lived through the European war, they would then continue fighting the Japanese.

We talked in our difficult way for a little while. I told them that I was a correspondent for a soldiers' magazine and asked if they could give me a story, for they must have many, having lived in Occupied France.

We shook hands. They told me their names: the little one was Roger; the others, Andre and Maurice. They came from the same small village in France. Roger, who acted as spokesman, was a

The clock tolled one hour, then another. These people had learned patience
during the war, were close to starvation and death, but this was too much.

youth who once must have been cherubic. He was not fat now, though a semblance of fleshiness was again filling out his bone structure. He said they would rather forget the time of the occupation, but that there was one story they could tell me.

It had happened in their native village, early in 1941 when the French people were in a bad way. The Germans had confiscated nearly all of the food. Pets had vanished from the village homes, having gone into the pots. Meat of any kind was unheard of. All the villagers were very close to starvation and death.

Then one morning in the local paper a startling notice appeared: "CITIZENS OF ——," it read. "TOMORROW MORNING AT 9:30 THERE WILL BE A DISTRIBUTION OF MEAT WITHOUT RATION COUPONS AT THE BUTCHER SHOP OF JEAN MARCEL."

Not many people slept that night. Those who weren't busy scurrying for francs were making their beds before Jean Marcel's shop so they would be first in line when his doors opened.

By sunup the villagers had formed double queues in front of the butcher shop. Everyone was talking; everyone was excited. They were almost happy.

Jean Marcel's shop stood in an open, unprotected place and the sun burned a path to his doorway. Finally, the clock in the ancient church struck the hour of 9 and, after what seemed an eternity, 9:30. But the door of the shop did not open. The people milled and muttered. An old woman at the head of the line began cursing, expressing the feelings of them all.

The clock tolled another hour, and another. These people had learned patience during the war, but this was too much. This was no time for Marcel to joke, growled the hungry.

Abruptly, angered beyond tolerance, they broke down the shop door with a great burst of strength.

Their free meat was hanging from the wall with a hook showing through its neck. It was a fat German captain, in full-dress uniform.

T/3 Jack Denton Scott

Sergeant John Denton Scott is a 29-year-old combat correspondent for Yank, *The Army Weekly*. He has seen service in England, the Middle East and Italy, and he has also viewed Germany from an American bomber.

Formerly a writer of detective fiction, Scott was inducted into the Army in March, 1941, from his home in Elmira, New York. He received his early training at Fort Bragg, North Carolina.

After a brief period in the magazine's home office he was sent to England, where he took an intensive training course in aerial gunnery. This qualified him to accompany the Air Force on some raids over Germany and Occupied Europe. His eyewitness accounts of these missions were published in Yank.

After a second period of service in the New York office, Scott was sent to the Middle East for the magazine. Later he acted as a combat correspondent with the Fifth Army in Italy.

Of himself, Scott says: "I have been a Yank *editor of the Middle*

East edition, seen and lived in Iceland, Greenland, Labrador, England, Scotland, Egypt, the Sudan, covered the continent of Africa — all for Yank. *I have two brothers—Lieutenant Craig Scott, also a writer, now with the Fifth Army, in the infantry; and Lieutenant Chester Scott, a pilot, somewhere in South America."*

"I DO IT FOR MY SISTER"

by Lloyd Shearer

I shall always remember the story of Paul Etienne's sister, Marie. To me it is the war's most moving account of self-sacrifice. I got the story from Paul when we were both in training at Fort Bragg. He told it to me one day on K. P. when I asked him why he was always volunteering for extra duty. "Don't you know?" I said, "In the Army, nobody volunteers."

Paul was tall and 28 years old. He smiled at me condescendingly, as if I could never understand him. "I do it for my sister, Marie," he explained.

Every time anyone asked Paul why he volunteered for guard duty, or charge of quarters—or anything else—it was always the same: "I do it for my sister, Marie."

That afternoon in the kitchen, Paul told me about Marie.

"She was 15 when I left Marseille in 1941," he began, "and when the Nazis overran France, she joined the Underground.

"She was very beautiful and strongly spirited, like a firm, fine colt. She had large, blue eyes and soft, blond hair and a very beautiful body, and the Underground leaders would not permit her to undertake any dangerous jobs. They used her as a messenger girl.

"When my two brothers were killed by the Gestapo for running an Underground paper, however, my sister went to another town and there begged the local leaders to give her more dangerous work. But she was so young, so pretty, so fragile and light that they were afraid. 'There are others to do this work, they told her.

102

"Perhaps Marie's eyes were too eager; perhaps they shone too brightly.
I don't know. . . . But somehow the Nazi became suspicious of my sister."

'Your time will come.' But Marie insisted, so they finally let her help derail trains by placing rocks on the rails at night.

"And then one day the report came into the Underground that the Gestapo leader at Champagnac—a man named Von Mannhertz, or something like that, and a clever, cruel beast—was murdering ten hostages a day.

"He had also succeeded in securing some vital information about the Underground. He must be destroyed, it was decided, whatever the cost.

"It was known that this beast had a weakness for pretty girls, and my sister pleaded for the job of ensnaring him. But the Underground would not hear of it. 'You are too young, too pretty,' the leaders told her. 'Your whole life lies ahead.' But Marie kept after them so persistently that eventually she got the assignment.

"She went to Champagnac, where this Gestapo brute, on the lookout for pretty young girls, spied her, ravaged her and then set her up as his mistress.

"One night when they were dining together alone, Marie dropped poison into his wine glass. He picked up the glass, and was about to drink the wine. Then he stopped. Perhaps Marie's eyes were too eager; perhaps they shone too brightly. I don't know. . . . But somehow the Nazi became suspicious and handed the glass to my sister.

" 'Let us share this,' he said. 'Half for you and half for me.'

"Marie smiled gaily and quite lightheartedly drank the poisoned wine. Then, still smiling, she handed the glass to the Gestapo barbarian, who downed the remainder.

"That is the story, told by the Gestapo leader's housekeeper, and brought to me in America by Pierre Grugere of the Belgian Underground."

Paul's eyes were filled with tears. "Now you understand," he said, "why I do all these things for my sister."

Lloyd Shearer

Five people were involved before this story by Shearer crossed LOOK's editorial desk.

The first was the Gestapo officer's housekeeper. She, in turn, told the story to members of the French Underground. One of them repeated it to Pierre Grugere, a leader in the Belgian Underground. Grugere, fleeing the Vichy police at the time, made a daring crossing of the English Channel with four other hunted men. He was the only one to reach England alive.

Eventually, Grugere was shipped to the United States for training in the Free French forces then being trained here. When he discovered that Paul Etienne was also in uniform, he sought him out and gave him the tragic details.

As Mr. Shearer states, it was from Paul himself that he heard the story of Marie's sacrifice.

Lloyd Shearer was born in New York in December, 1917. His father was a newspaperman and his grandfather a printer—which may account for his interest in writing.

He was reared in North Carolina, where he started writing for pulp magazines and state papers at the age of 16. Shearer was graduated from the University of North Carolina at 19 and taught for a time at Louisiana State University.

He next worked for the Washington Post, then joined an advertising agency, where he wrote radio scripts during the day and free-lanced in his spare time.

His short stories and articles have appeared in Collier's, Liberty, The Saturday Evening Post, Reader's Digest, LOOK, The New York Times, Good Housekeeping and other publications. His radio scripts have been heard on all the major networks.

One of the first men to enter the Army under Selective Service, he was assigned to Yank, The Army Weekly, as a roving correspondent. Later, he was transferred to the Armed Forces Radio Service.

ACTION IN VELA GULF

by Pat Robinson

I have had the good luck to go along on some 40 bombing and strafing raids on Jap positions. I have been in nine amphibious landings on enemy-held islands and in two infantry campaigns. I have seen dozens of aerial dogfights and been under scores of Japanese strafing and bombing raids.

All of these were exciting, but none gave me half the thrill I got in the Battle of Vela Gulf where Admiral Halsey's destroyers sank a cruiser and three destroyers without injury to an American boy or ship.

The battle took place the night of August 7, 1943. I was aboard the *Lang,* one of our little 1,700-ton destroyers, skippered by Commander John Lester Wilfong. We had sped north from Guadalcanal looking for trouble and Japs. Within a few hours we found both.

I never saw the sea around the Solomon Islands as rough as it was that night. A gale whipped the waves to a fury and as we slipped past little Gizo Island we ran into a tropical downpour that stung our faces like hail.

When all hands were ordered to battle stations, I regretfully left an acey-deucey game in the wardroom and raced up to the bridge, where Commander Rodger Simpson was shouting a stream of orders over the inter-ship communication system.

It was so dark I couldn't see the outline of the destroyer directly ahead of us. I couldn't even distinguish the faces of the men beside me on the bridge. But I recognized Simpson's voice above

106

The resulting explosion was terrific as the 20-foot tin fish hit the Jap cruiser.
A wall of flame shot up, throwing the enemy destroyers into bold relief.

the roaring of the gale.

Commander Simpson is one of the most friendly officers who ever came out of Annapolis. He is a minister's son, with a reputation for never using strong language. That is, he did have the reputation but, to the amazement, admiration and unbounded joy of every man of us, he lost it that night. It was later agreed that no stevedore, no truck driver, not even Admiral Halsey himself, had ever used saltier language.

Simpson was indignant when we told him some of the words he had used during the heat of battle. "Why," he protested, "I never used such language in my life!"

At 11 o'clock we were well into the 12-mile channel that separates the islands of Kolombangara and Vela Lavella. Although only a few hundred yards off shore, we couldn't see Kolombangara's mountains. Rain beat down furiously, wind howled and the ship rolled through an infuriated sea.

It was exactly 11:37 p. m. when a thrill ran through the task force. Our radar had picked up four Jap warships—a cruiser and destroyer escort—but the first intimation they had of our presence was when our torpedoes and shells ploughed into them.

We fired our first torpedoes at the cruiser—the largest and most valuable of the four targets. The 20-foot tin fish sped through the boiling sea as surely as if guided by hand. There was a terrific explosion and a wall of flame shot up, throwing the enemy ships into bold relief.

A moment later every gun on our ships cut loose, pouring salvo after salvo of 5-inch shells into the enemy. The green tracers made a gorgeous pattern in the darkness. They looked like a series of green neon lights moving lazily through the night.

The Jap return fire fell harmlessly among our ships and the enemy guns were quickly silenced. By now all four Jap ships were burning fiercely, flames shooting a hundred feet into the sky. Burning oil on the water made a continuous line of fire from the bow of the first ship to the stern of the last.

We were all screaming like madmen and one youngster beside me kept yelling over and over, "Roast, you rats, roast!" I found

108

myself laughing wildly and pounding Commander Simpson on the back. He didn't seem to mind. He'd take a look at the burning ships, then yell another order.

Now we closed in on the enemy. One Jap destroyer was already dead in the water and burning fiercely. Next came a great explosion aboard the cruiser and she began to sink, bow first. Moments later all four ships were obviously headed for the bottom. We raced to within a hundred yards of the doomed vessels, then cut our engines. All around in the blazing sea we could see hundreds of soldiers. The warships had been carrying troops, apparently to reinforce Kolombangara and Vela Lavella.

Simpson was eager to get prisoners. He ordered life lines thrown out—but not one Jap took a line! So he ordered full speed ahead and we ploughed on through the screaming men.

When daylight came our PT boats found hundreds of corpses washed up on the beach of Vela Lavella.

Pat Robinson

Rugged veteran of 30 years of newspaper work, Pat Robinson has covered everything from baseball to battlefronts. A soldier in World War I, he later did sports reporting for several New York dailies, and in 1931 joined International News Service.

After Pearl Harbor he covered the bitterly fought Papuan campaign, was the first newsman to go on a bombing mission over Rabaul, knows what it is to make a crash landing. With 14 months of war behind him, he wrote a book, The Fight for New Guinea. *Reassigned to the Pacific, he covered the Solomon Islands, was twice commended for aiding the wounded under fire.*

ENSIGN WITH NINE LIVES

by Ira Wolfert

Shortly after the carrier *Wasp* was sunk, I arrived in the New Hebrides in a Flying Fortress whose bombardier was Lieutenant Robert Mitchell.

Mitch had not seen his kid brother, John Jenks Mitchell, in two years. Now was his chance. John Jenks, 21 years old and not long out of Annapolis, had been an ensign on the *Wasp* and was now in a New Hebrides hospital awaiting transportation south.

We all went along with Mitch. When we got to the Quonset hut where John Jenks was, we found the boy lying quietly under a ferocious beard, his leg stretched out in one of those grisly chromium and plaster, sandbagged contraptions.

John Jenks had to lie flat on his back. He could barely turn his head, but he saw Mitch.

"Why, you old, no-good son of a gun!" he said.

"You gob-eared so-and-so!" Mitch replied, and they shook hands in a way fonder than kissing, each very close to tears.

When Mitch asked what had happened, the boy said: "There was a loud noise. Something like a railroad train going up a flight of iron stairs. Then it was ten days later and I wanted a cigarette. That's the whole story."

But there was more to it than that. And shipmates in near-by beds began to fill in some of the events that lay between the noise and the cigarette.

"As a matter of fact," John Jenks interrupted in his dry, quiet voice, "this ward has been something like a fraternity house on

110

"There was a loud noise, something like a railroad train going up a flight of stairs. I started for the pearly gates but God stopped me in mid-air."

the morning after, each man telling what he did while under the influence—the influence in this case being high explosives."

The first torpedo to hit the *Wasp* came in right under the feet of Ensign Mitchell, whose gun station on the aircraft carrier was on a thin-skinned deck right over a 1,000-pound bomb. The torpedo, the bomb, the gun and its crew all went up together.

"I started for the pearly gates," John Jenks said, "but God put his hand on my shoulder and stopped me in mid-air." The ensign was very serious when he said that. Then he grinned. "I thereupon landed on the bridge, smack at the feet of my superiors, in a posture unbecoming a junior officer—flat on my back."

John Jenks laughed so hard that the whole contraption around his leg shook. But no one else laughed.

"How far was the bridge from your gun station?" his brother asked, unsmilingly.

A wounded damage control officer, familiar with the *Wasp's* measurements, supplied the answer. The bridge was more than thirty feet above and sixty feet away from the spot where Ensign Mitchell had been standing when the torpedo hit. This started a voluminous argument, in which everyone joined, as to whether Ensign Mitchell was entitled to the world's record for the involuntary standing high jump. As far as the Mitchells and their friends could discover, John Jenks' nearest competitor was an American in the last war, name unknown to them, who had been blown thirty feet into the air by a shell but had landed only a few feet from his take-off point.

"Anyway," John Jenks pointed out, laughing, "I can now put in my chit to qualify for landings on the flight deck."

When the ensign landed on the bridge, he was considerably more dead than alive. The chances are a doctor would have passed him up as a bad risk. But there were no doctors on the bridge. So Lieutenant Courtney Shands dropped from the bridge to the explosive murk below, where airplanes and their ammunition were popping like balloons on New Year's Eve, and dug a raft from a plane. Then he and Commander Beakley strapped the unconscious boy to the raft and lowered it to the calm sea.

112

But the raft was topheavy and turned over, its occupant tightly secured under some half dozen feet of sea that was full of sharks which had been attracted by the bloody gruel about the *Wasp.*

In this crisis, with everybody under great temptation to get away from the sharks, and the sinking vessel and the exploding bombs, Lieutenant Robert Slye struggled with the raft until he had righted it, taking time out every now and then to thrash at the sharks with his feet.

The last I heard, John Jenks, by then a lieutenant, was nearly as good as ever, and his brother Mitch was as good as ever, too. About ten days after this story was told, Mitch was deposited in the same Quonset hut and in the same bed. But he could not claim the world's record for the involuntary standing high jump. He had merely stopped about thirty fragments from a Jap explosive bullet.

Ira Wolfert

Ira Wolfert is one of those fabulous rarities, a native New Yorker. He earned his way through the Columbia School of Journalism by working as a taxi driver and as a streetcar motorman.

In 1930, he joined the North American Newspaper Alliance, then went to Europe, representing the New York Post *in Berlin.*

In 1942, NANA assigned Wolfert to the Solomons and his experiences there are described in his books, Battle for the Solomons *(which won the Pulitzer Prize in 1942), and* Torpedo 8. *On a second trip to the Solomons, in 1943, he was stricken with malaria after seven months.*

In 1944, he covered the Western Front, traveling into Germany. Back in the U.S. after nine months, he wrote American Guerrilla in the Philippines, *a selection of the Book-of-the-Month Club.*

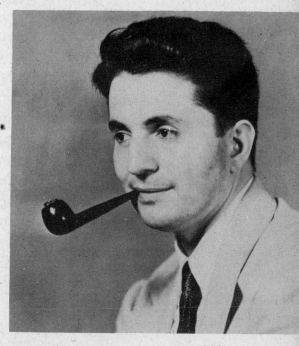

PISTOL PACKIN' SISTER

by John W. Jarrell

My friend Liang, who told me this story over the hubbub of a crowded Chinese cafe, is a man who gets around. I had just finished telling him what I'd like to do to the Japanese. When I was through, he said:

"The trouble is, you just *tell* what you'd like to do. You ought to be more like Two Gun Sister Wang. She doesn't say much—but I hear that after her latest exploit the Japs have raised the price on her head."

So I pumped Liang, whose activities include a little of everything from genteel gambling to some two-fisted smuggling. And in the cafe, surrounded by natives whose noisy eating habits brought us a measure of privacy, Liang told me the most surprising story of any I have heard about the fabled Two Gun Sister Wang.

The Japanese, Liang said, three times have raised their reward offer for the capture, dead or alive, of Sister Wang, who wears two guns strapped to her shapely hips and leads a desperate guerrilla band in Kiangsu and Chekiang provinces.

"The last time they raised their price on her head," he said, taking a sip of his drink and smacking his lips, "they proved that they have absolutely no sense of humor. Sister Wang played a joke on them—and they didn't see anything funny about it."

I had heard a lot of stories about Sister Wang, but I had been suspicious of them until the official Chinese press association, Central News, one day reported one of her exploits. So now I listened with interest to Liang.

114

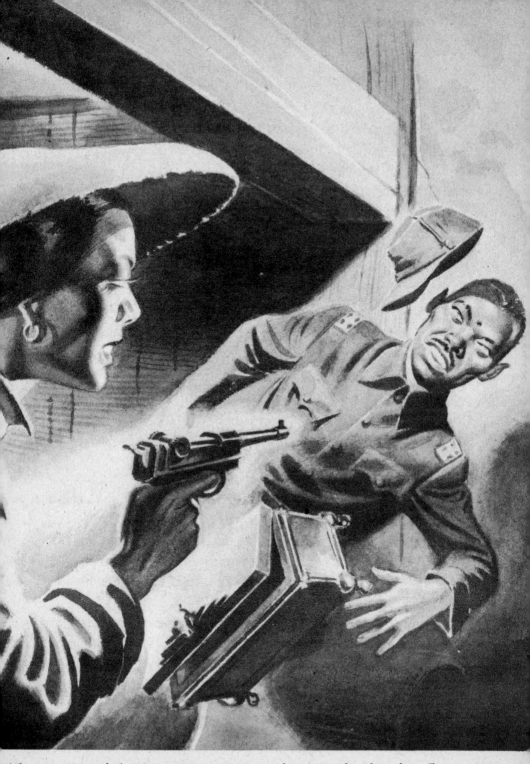

That was enough for Sister Wang. Drawing her gun, she shot the officer between the eyes. One less Jap — but a body that would cause trouble.

Sister Wang, Liang said, is a good-looking woman in her low thirties and she likes to visit Shangai now and then. She has friends there and, despite the presence of thousands of Japanese soldiers, she goes in and out as she pleases. She made her last trip to that enemy-held city only recently. At night, accompanied only by two of her male guerrilla followers, she walked through darkened streets of the native city and made her way to a certain house, which served as her headquarters when she was in Shanghai.

The next day, still escorted, she strolled down Nanking Road for a rare orgy of window shopping. She was now wearing conventional Chinese clothes—plus a gun in a special shoulder holster. At one shop she paused, looked in, then entered.

Inside a Japanese officer was telling the Chinese salesman that he would take along a handsome teakwood chest—and pay later. When the clerk protested against this obvious theft, the Japanese slapped him. That was enough for Sister Wang. Drawing her gun, she shot the officer between the eyes.

So, one less Japanese—but a body that would cause trouble for the Chinese clerk. Quickly, Sister Wang had her henchmen wrap the corpse in rags and carry it out the back way.

Through the teeming streets and alleys that she knew so well, Sister Wang led the little procession. No one paid any attention to them; dead bodies are commonplace in Shanghai these days.

Back in her temporary headquarters, Sister Wang held a grim conference. When night fell, her two escorts slipped out again. In half an hour they returned with one live, blindfolded and panic-stricken Japanese soldier.

Some time later Sister Wang, her bodyguards and some of her Shanghai followers stole forth once more. With them were the two Japs—one dead, one alive. Later they came back—without the Japs.

In the early morning a crowd gathered just off Bubbling Well Road, near the race course. Soon the Japanese military arrived on the scene. What they saw will live forever in Chinese legend. Seated in a ricksha, bound and gagged, was a Japanese soldier. Propped between the shafts, with a coolie hat shading his sightless eyes

116

but otherwise in his imperial uniform, was a dead Japanese officer

Talk about loss of face—an imperial Japanese officer serving as a ricksha coolie!

Of course, the soldier soon sputtered out the whole story. And Two Gun Sister Wang? She got away unscathed. The best the Japs could do was to raise the already high price on her head.

I just hope she still carries on. Pistol-packin' Sister, don't lay that pistol down!

John W. Jarrell

John W. Jarrell's father published a weekly newspaper in Holton, Kansas, and there the son early acquired a taste for printer's ink.

Starting as a cub reporter on the Topeka (Kansas) State Journal, he worked on several papers in the Mid-West and the East and eventually found his way to Shanghai, China, where he joined the staff of the Evening Post and Mercury. Later, he was employed by International News Service.

Jarrell has always had an itching foot. He once worked his way to China aboard a ship (1928); again, four years later, he made a tramp tour through the Balkans, the Middle East and North Africa.

Jarrell was on the INS cable desk in New York when this country entered the war. His first overseas assignment was the invasion of North Africa, which he covered with Patton's task force. Following that, he spent a full year in the China-Burma-India theater.

After a rest in the United States, he was detailed to England and he covered the Normandy invasion as

the only press association representative of the U.S.S. Augusta, the American flagship which had General Bradley aboard.

Jarrell returned to the U. S. late in July, 1944.

Thereupon he left INS and returned to his native Mid-West, becoming a staff member on the Omaha World-Herald.

THE PRISONER RESCUES HIS CAPTOR

by Bela Balazs

No writer could ever invent such a story—only life can be so improbable. So I would like to make it clear first of all that this incident really took place, and that the man who experienced it is now in a military hospital. He is Senior Lieutenant Issambayev, of the Red Army, a Kazakh by nationality.

The story takes place in the winter of 1942, near Voronezh, where half the Hungarian Army was wiped out. Issambayev was out on an important scouting assignment. A Hungarian Honved regiment had taken up positions in a certain woods, and it was necessary to locate their machine gun and mortar batteries before the Soviet attack.

The muffling silence of the thick snow made any sharp sound ring out with particular clarity. In order to reduce the sound of their movement to a minimum, Issambayev ordered the men of his scouting squad to keep at a distance of three hundred paces from one another. Each had his dagger loose in its sheath, for under no conditions could they risk the sound of gunfire that would warn the enemy of their presence.

In the sector he had chosen, Issambayev discovered two machine guns and one mortar. He was about to return when he caught and wrenched his ankle in a snow-covered hole. The pain was so intense that Issambayev was barely able to draw his foot out again.

The young Kazakh's swarthy face, with the prominent cheekbones and narrow eyes, grew rigid with pain. For the present there could be no question of walking.

118

Evening was falling when, laughing and shouting, the Russian soldiers came running up to the headquarters to witness a strange spectacle.

He knew that somewhere, three hundred paces away, his ser-geant, Belchivok, was crawling through the wood, but he also knew he could not call for aid. The slightest sound would reach the Hungarian outposts—who would investigate before Belchikov could reach him. There was nothing to do but wait. When his patrol returned without him, a search would be made and he would be found.

The Kazakh lieutenant barely had time to reason this out when he heard snow crunching and dry twigs snapping. Someone was approaching. One of his comrades? That would be luck!

There . . . behind the bush . . . a helmet under a hood. . . . Issambayev recognized the shape at once; it was a Hungarian soldier he saw, a Honved.

The Honved had not yet noticed him, and had it not been for that accursed foot, he could have hurled himself at the man and settled the issue with his dagger.

Raising his tommy gun—although he knew that to shoot was out of the question—the lieutenant hissed: "Hands up!"

It was only then that the Honved saw him. The Kazakh's hard, implacable face had an even stronger effect on the young soldier than the menace of the gun. He immediately threw away his rifle and raised his arms.

"I surrender voluntarily! I have come over voluntarily!" he cried. The Russian phrases he had previously prepared came tumbling out in his haste. "I will no longer . . . ."

"Silence!" Issambayev commanded.

The boy's words died away. He really was a boy, barely twenty, with something childlike in his expression. Fear flickered in his eyes. His pale lips wore a helpless, pleading smile. He did indeed look as though he had been waiting for a chance to give himself up.

So far, so good. Senior Lieutenant Issambayev had taken a prisoner—but what in the world was he to do with him? The conqueror's main problem was to hide his helplessness from his prisoner. The Hungarian continued to stand in front of Issambayev with raised arms.

Meanwhile an artillery duel had begun. Heavy shells were screaming over their heads, sometimes carrying away a treetop.

The prisoner once more became uneasy. He stared with increasing fear at the inexorably hard, narrow-eyed face of his captor. Why was he not taken to headquarters? Could it be true, as the German officers had told him, that the Reds take no prisoners? He did not believe that the Russians killed those who voluntarily surrendered. But this narrow-eyed, brown-faced man was no Russian; he was a Tartar or something of that kind. It was his misfortune that he had been captured by some half-wild Asiatic. Could understanding be expected from such a man?

Issambayev peered right and left, as though awaiting the arrival of some of his men, but the movement caused him sudden pain in his injured leg. His face involuntarily contorted and a groan escaped his lips.

The prisoner looked at the leg in surprise. Evidently suspicion had dawned on him. Issambayev knew his attention must be distracted. He asked a question at random.

"How did you come to learn Russian?"

"Unfortunately I know only a little," the lad replied hastily. It was a relief when this terrible Asiatic asked him a sensible question. "I come from north Hungary where the Carpathian Russians live. I hoped to use the unfortunate Russian campaign to learn the language better."

"The language of the people whom you torture and kill?" Issambayev interrupted roughly.

"The Germans . . ." the Honved began in fresh alarm, "the Germans . . . ."

"And not the Hungarians? Worse, if anything!"

The young fellow paled. "I . . . I didn't want . . ." he stuttered. "It was for that reason I came over. I am . . . ."

"What were you before the war?" asked Issambayev, still talking to gain time.

"A university student of Budapest."

"Which faculty?"

The Honved, who had been speaking with eyes cast down, suddenly raised his head in surprise. Incredulously he stared at the Russian commander. Was it "faculty" the man had said? A Bolshevik talking about faculties!

"The philological faculty," he replied hesitatingly.

"Have you studied Hungarian philology?"

The prisoner let both arms drop, despite orders to the contrary. He was so taken aback that he forgot all about the gun. As though held by a magnet, his eyes were fixed steadily on the metallically hard Asiatic face.

"Yes," the prisoner replied at last. "Hungarian philology is my main subject."

"Which course are you in?"

"The sixth."

"Have you attended Professor Nemeth's lectures?"

The student at first found it impossible to reply. It was incredible! He rubbed his forehead.

"Yes, yes!" he cried finally.

"Quiet!" The command was no longer threatening, but almost friendly. This gave the student courage to ask a question himself.

"How do you know about Professor Nemeth?" he asked.

A faint smile passed over the Asiatic's hard face. "I received my last letter from him two months before the war broke out."

"Letter?"

"I am also a professor of philology at the Kazakh University in Alma-Ata. I'm studying the relationship between the Kazakh and the Hungarian languages."

"But then we must be . . ." the student stammered, "we must be of the same race, if our theory is correct."

A shell whizzed down somewhere near. Old pines splintered, crashed one on top of another, raising clouds of snow as their long roots were ripped from the frozen soil.

The Honved swiftly flattened himself; the lieutenant tried to do the same, but his injured leg hindered him.

Again the prisoner's attention was drawn to the leg. Crouching on the ground, squinting sideways at the lieutenant, he said: "Herr Professor, you have injured your leg. If you cannot walk, I will help you."

122

And that was what actually happened. It was no simple matter and it took time. The young Honved could not walk with the Russian lieutenant on his back all the way. The firing was increasing in intensity on both sides. The only way to cross open spaces was by crawling.

Evening was already falling when, with much shouting and laughter, Russian soldiers came running up to divisional headquarters to witness a strange spectacle.

A Hungarian prisoner was carrying on his back the Red officer who had captured him.

"Who's that bringing you in, Issambayev?" they asked.

"A relative," was the calm reply.

Bela Balazs

Bela Balazs is the son of a college professor who lived in a small town in Hungary.

His early life was not easy; from the age of 14 he had to earn his own living. Despite his lack of funds, however, he managed to study philosophy and philology in Budapest, Berlin and Paris. Even at that early date, the excellence of his poetry won wide attention.

Balazs' first play was staged at the Budapest National Theater when the author was 25. Eventually, because of a mounting reactionary sentiment in Hungary, and because of his own liberal thought, he was forced to flee to Vienna, where he found it necessary to live under a fictitious name.

In 1931, he adopted the Soviet Union as his homeland. There, he wrote the first part of his major novel, Youth of a Dreamer, as well as a number of plays and short stories. He is now in Alma-Ata, Russia, where he wrote The Prisoner Rescues His Captor.

THE COLONEL BAGS A NAZI

by Cpl. Bill Barrett

For 39 years of army life, through two world wars, Colonel Robert Sears had fretted behind a desk far in the rear of any fighting. He had wanted front-line action. He had wanted to kill a German. Now, as retirement loomed, he decided he was going to do it.

He asked for a transfer to an infantry regiment on the Italian front. Nothing happened. He pressed for the transfer. It was denied. Instead, Colonel Sears was sent to an ordnance unit, nearer the front than he had been, but still far to the rear of any real fighting. He wasn't irked, though, as he might have been, because he felt he was getting there.

At the ordnance outfit he asked permission to take a new sniper's rifle up to the Anzio-Nettuno beachhead to see how it met combat conditions. The request was granted, and the old colonel smiled.

Once in the Anzio sector, he took the new rifle to the range of one of the infantry divisions. The doughfeet there watched him assume the position, a little stiffly, and let go with a few rounds. The result was very poor. The colonel knew he wasn't the man he once was, but he didn't think he was bad enough to miss the target completely at 500 yards. He decided the rifle was at fault.

It was. He borrowed an old Springfield, took off his helmet, took off his glasses, lay down and shot a couple of bull's eyes. Then to make sure he could drill them with his tin hat on, he replaced his helmet and hit the middle of the target again.

124

After his waiting, his chance had come. The German became careless, exposed half his body. The colonel snuggled the Springfield to his chest.

This time the colonel grinned openly. He was ready.

He hitched a ride through rain and mud to a front-line regiment. There he got transportation to a battalion, then to a line company. At that point they tried to talk him out of going on. He was old, and it was raining hard.

But the colonel was a fast talker, too, and if he pulled his rank here, it was in a good cause. He stumbled out into the dark with a guide. He fell several times. And when he finally reached the foxhole of Staff Sergeant Primitnic Vialpando, he was drenched.

The old colonel and the sergeant lay in the wet darkness for many hours, and then the sun came up. It was warmer now, and light.

Colonel Sears sighted his German about 6:30 in the morning. The Nazi was lying out in a draw, and the rising sun glinted for just a moment on his helmet as he raised his head.

The colonel settled down to waiting. The German would stick his head up a few inches, then jerk it down. The colonel was patient as he watched for his chance. He had already waited 39 years.

Then his chance came. The German became careless, exposed half his body. The colonel snuggled the Springfield up to his cheek, looked down the sights at the German tunic and squeezed the trigger.

Colonel Sears had his German. . . .

He ought to have been ready to go home then, but there was still fire in his eye.

"I want to go on a bombing mission before I get home," he said. "I have a son in the air forces, and I don't intend to listen to his stories for the rest of my life. And, if I have anything to say about it, I won't be retired right away. I've got to get out to the Pacific, too!"

Cpl. Bill Barrett

In June, 1941, at the age of 20, Bill Barrett joined the staff of the Cleveland Press and 14 months later entered the Army. After basic training, he was transferred to the staff of the 45th Division News, the first paper ever printed by an invasion force on Axis soil—Sicily. The 45th Division fought through many of the major battles in Italy and was in the midst of the struggle at Anzio.

"Our print shop in Palermo was a smoking ruin when we moved in," says Barrett. "It was still a smoking ruin when we moved out a few weeks later, after publishing our first edition. The edition contained art, with engravings etched on the only zinc available—the lining of a coffin!"

In August, 1944, the 45th left Italy, becoming part of the Seventh Army. Barrett participated in the invasion of France and the final struggle inside Germany.

TWO TANKS AND A JEEP

by Edward Gottlieb

G.I.'s and American officers alike have always talked with respect and admiration for the Combat Supply Service boys — the truck drivers and the two-fisted, fearless troops who deliver the weapons to our fighting men at the front. The reputation of these men was at its height in the days of the big Normandy break-through.

General Patton's Third Army had just gone into action against the Germans on the southern fringe of the Falaise pocket while another arm of his forces poured through the narrow opening in the Normandy peninsula and wheeled to trap the Germans in Brittany. Against this setting of plunging, shifting armies, it was often difficult to know whether you were in territory safely held by American troops or being "zeroed" by German 88's hidden by the hedgerows.

So it was with some uneasiness that I started one afternoon in August, 1944, from Colombières in Normandy for General Patton's command post. Private Charles Timm, my jeep driver, tore along the pitted roads, making turns only after I had carefully checked my map.

All I knew about finding Third Army H.Q. was that it was near Beauchamp—and near some heavy fighting. Approaching darkness made Timm slow the jeep. There was another reason too. We were alone on the road. We knew that where there were no supply trucks, convoys or ambulances there usually was danger.

We were going up a long hill when I saw something on the crest.

"Charlie," I yelled, "take it up to 50!" But even at 50, and then at 60 miles an hour, the speeding tanks roared thunderously close behind.

"Stop!" I yelled. "A couple of tanks dead ahead!"

Timm jammed the brakes on and skidded the jeep into a thick hedgerow. We were out of the car instantly and flat on our stomachs. Seconds and minutes passed without a sound from the tanks. I pulled the branches aside slightly.

"Gee whizz, Charlie," I whispered, after looking hard for a moment, "these are U. S. tanks. I'm going out there and find out what the hell they're doing parked in the middle of the road."

A front slit was open in the nearest tank. I looked inside, straight into the surprised face of a Negro G.I. He was alone in the tank and I could see sweat glisten on his face in the dim light.

"What the hell are you doing blocking the road?" I yelled.

A broad smile lighted his face. "Sir," he said, "we're sure glad to see you. We're lost—me and my partner in the other tank."

"Where are you headed for?" I asked.

"We're looking for the Third Army, to deliver these tanks, sir."

I thought for a moment, then said: "That's where I'm going, too. You follow us."

Timm had already pulled the jeep out of the hedge. The roar of the two tank engines filled the air ahead of us, and I was comforted. Having two tanks with us would help—especially in case we ran into any trouble.

We drove out in front of them. I could hear them picking up speed.

"Timm," I said, "I don't know anything about tanks. Better try holding your speed to 25 miles an hour so they can keep up with us."

After a few minutes I looked back. The first big tank was roaring along not more than 15 feet behind us.

"Charlie," I said, trying to hide my concern, "that tank's too close. Try 35." The jeep jumped ahead.

After a little while I looked around a second time. The damned monsters were right up on our rear again.

"Charlie," I yelled, out-shouting the thunderous tank exhausts, "we'll both be flatter than a waffle if you have to stop suddenly. Take it up to 50."

130

But even at 50, and then at 60 miles an hour, the tanks roared close behind. As we approached the Third Army area, M.P.'s gave us the right of way, certain that our thunderous convoy was headed straight for action. Now it took Timm two miles of gradual slowing down to get us stopped safely. I jumped out.

"Well, here we are," I said to the boy I'd talked to before.

"Yes sir. Thank you, sir."

"Where'd you come from with these tanks?"

The colored boy's eyes widened. "From Scotland, sir. They just put us on a big boat, then on a small one, and when we come off we was told to drive 'em to the Third Army."

"What kind of tank is this?"

"A medium tank, I guess, sir."

"How fast will it go?"

"Sir," the boy said earnestly, his eyes big as banjos, "I really don't know. This is the first time I ever drove one."

Edward Gottlieb

In 1933—while studying medicine at the University of Goettingen, in Germany—Ed Gottlieb witnessed the torture of several Jews by the Nazis and resolved to become a newspaperman to fight the rising Nazi menace. Both United Press and International News Service accepted him as Berlin correspondent.

He returned to New York, his birthplace, two years later. INS put him on the foreign desk. When we entered the war, he joined the OWI.

Gottlieb headed the combat team for Psychological Warfare with General Patton's Third Army.

Mustered out of the OWI as a casualty, Gottlieb returned to this country early in 1945.

SWIMMING SURGEON

by Robert Eunson

Our destroyer was cutting a silvery furrow in the black waters south of New Britain as we took position for the predawn attack on the beaches of Arawe.

"Did you have to come?" asked the little doctor standing at the rail.

"All war correspondents are volunteers," I told him, leaning over to watch the phosphorescent path of the destroyer's hull as it slid through the warm salt water of the Bismarck Sea.

I was nervous and felt the need of conversation. "What kind of doctor were you before the war?" I asked. "I mean, what was your practice?"

"Obstetrics," he answered, his voice soft and clear against the whir of the diesels. "Delivered babies in Little Rock."

I pulled a notebook from the pocket of my green coveralls and wrote down his name and home town: Captain Charles P. Wickard, Little Rock, Arkansas.

"You never can tell," I said. "A doctor in New Guinea—Joseph R. Strauss, of Bridgeport—gave me a pip of a story. He saved two men with brain surgery at Tsili Tsili. Right on the field. Operated with tools from his field kit while the medics chased the mosquitoes away and held candles over the litter he was using for an operating table. Maybe you'll give me a story tomorrow."

Captain Wickard took off his cap and smiled as he ran his fingers through his short blond hair. "I hope not," he said, his voice serious. "I hope there isn't a Jap on the island."

132

For three hours, the little doctor swam from boat to boat, jabbing morphine needles into the jerking bodies of wounded survivors, easing their pain.

133

For ten days we had been training for this strike with the 112th Cavalry—the old Texas National Guard—commanded by Brigadier General Julian Cunningham. Captain Wickard and I were with a commando unit led by Captain Ed Wright, of Dallas. Wright's job was to sneak ashore at the base of the peninsula with 150 men one hour before the main landing on the peninsula's tip. We were to divert the Japanese from the main beachhead.

We went into the rubber boats at 5:02 a.m., December 15, 1943. None of us—the ones still alive—will ever forget that date. When our 10-man rubber boats were 35 yards from the white, sandy beach, the Japanese opened up on us with five machine guns and a 37 mm. cannon. They sank 10 of our 15 boats and killed about half the unit of 150 men. We never did get ashore. Lieutenant Joe Batz, of Bryan, Texas, was the only man who even got his feet on the bottom.

The Japs kept us in that horrible cross fire for 22 minutes until a destroyer wheeled in 1,000 yards from shore and sent its five-inchers, white hot and glowing, chunking into the beach. After that we got the wounded into the boats, peeled off our clothes, cut off our jungle boots and began pushing the boats out to sea.

Corporal Roy C. Jackson of Dallas was in charge of our boat. We had three wounded men aboard, lying face down, their pitiful groans audible above all the other sounds of our retreat.

Then I saw the doctor.

Wickard came swimming through the dawn. He was using a crawl stroke, progressing easily and slowly. He still wore his green jungle clothes. They clung heavily to his body.

"Any wounded?" he asked, resting against the outer rim of the deflating, bullet-punctured craft.

We nodded and he pulled himself up on the edge. Then he reached down in his pocket and pulled out a tiny syringe, a *syrette,* good for only one shot of morphine and then to be thrown away. He jabbed the needle into the buttocks of the man nearest him and pressed down the plunger. Then he did the same for the others. They jerked slightly at the sting of the needle, turned glassy eyes as he spoke encouragingly.

134

Once when Wickard couldn't reach clear across the boat to drive the needle into one of our wounded, I saw Corporal Jackson lift the little doctor and hoist him over the side.

One of the boys in our boat was a Mexican. He was tall and strong, and a favorite with the others. His skull was cracked wide open and he had a hole through his right cheek. His head was covered with caked blood and one eye was locked shut. But he managed to smile at Wickard.

After treating our men, Wickard swam away to another boat. He went slowly, his tousled blond head rolling from side to side.

For three hours he did that, working from boat to boat, while we marveled at his courage and endurance. Meantime, the Mexican and our two other wounded boys went to sleep, their pain forgotten in the dreams Wickard's drug had brought them.

Just before a subchaser picked us up we made Wickard get into our rubber boat. Jackson helped him in with a strong, brotherly shove that made me glad my eyes were filled with salt water anyway.

Robert Eunson

Robert Eunson was educated at Virginia Military Institute and Arizona State Teachers College. His hometown is Billings, Montana.

In March, 1941, after a period as editor of small Western newspapers and as an instructor at Arizona State, he joined the staff of the Associated Press, and in June, 1943, became one of its foreign correspondents.

He was in the Southwest Pacific for 14 months, until August, 1944, when malaria forced him to return. But after a month's rest he was away again, bound for the European theater where he covered the operations of the U.S. Ninth Army.

UNSCHEDULED SOLO

by Jack Mahon

H e saw his pilot get a slug through the head and slump forward over the controls—dead. Now he was alone in the tail of a lurching dive bomber over Munda Bay—and he had never flown a plane!

That's the spot in which Marine Sergeant Gilbert H. Henze, 24, of State Center, Iowa, found himself during a particularly heavy raid on the Munda airfield on New Georgia Island in the South Pacific.

Henze was the rear gunner in a Douglas Dauntless bomber, one of the flight attacking the airfield, then in Jap, now in American, hands. The flight had arrived high over the target and the lead planes started to dive. Henze's pilot did not follow them. Shrapnel had pierced the cockpit and killed him instantly.

Henze had no way of reaching his dead companion. Alone in the wobbling ship, he seized the controls in his rear gun station and managed to keep the plane in level flight. Then he started calling on his radio. As the sweat poured down his neck, Henze managed to establish contact with the leader of a flight of fighter planes. He explained his predicament and asked for instructions.

The fighter pilot immediately swung close to Henze's ship and there, thousands of feet over the ocean, ensued probably the quickest and certainly one of the most dramatic course of aeronautical instruction in history.

"Now proceed southeast," instructed the fighter pilot when Henze had got the feel of his plane.

He remembered little of what happened after that. The following six hours were a gory nightmare of unconsciousness, weariness and pain.

137

"But I haven't a compass," protested Henze. "All instruments are up ahead."

"Then follow the island route back. It leads straight to Guadalcanal. I'll go right along with you."

Limping through the sky, which to one was home and to the other a vast trackless void, the two planes inched back toward their base. The roundabout miles were filled with tortuous uncertainty, for Henze's ship—piloted by a dead man, a novice and a voice—was never under firm control. Suddenly Henze's motor began to sputter.

"I'm running out of gas," he told his guardian.

"Open your reserve tank," the fighter pilot directed.

Henze searched desperately. It was useless; he couldn't locate the switch. He called again to his guide, but he got no reply. The fighter's radio had failed. Henze was on his own.

He had only one chance—to bail out. He put the plane into a dive—he should have climbed—and jumped.

Before he could carom clear of the twitching plane, a tail stabilizer struck his leg. Agonizing pain shot through his body.

Henze jerked frantically at the rip cord, then, swaying on the lines like a bloody puppet, pressed his hands on the main artery of what had been his leg—now all but severed.

The boy remembered little of what happened after that. The following six hours were a gory nightmare of unconsciousness, of weariness and pain. It finally ended when black faces peered out of a fog, and friendly hands lifted him into a canoe.

The rescue party proved to be natives from the Russell Islands, northwest of Guadalcanal. They took the wounded Marine ashore and nursed him—as they have so many American fliers who have been forced down in the Solomon Islands—until a Navy rescue plane arrived and took Henze to Tulagi for treatment.

Sergeant Henze lost his leg, but his performance won a great boon for his buddies. Now all rear seat men are given sufficient instruction to enable them to fly in an emergency. Thus, if a pilot is wounded, a gunner can fly the plane back to base—saving two valuable lives, as well as $75,000 worth of aircraft.

138

Jack Mahon

Jack Mahon has done more traveling in the past decade than most men do in a lifetime. With the New York Daily News from 1933 to 1941, he did feature and sports writing, covering a nation-wide beat and reporting major sports events from the Rose Bowl to the Kentucky Derby.

In 1941, he joined the International News Service and in 1943 was assigned to the South Pacific area as a war correspondent. He returned after eight months, then undertook a second Pacific assignment in 1944 and a third in 1945. Of his experiences as a war correspondent, Mahon says:

"I have been with every branch of the service but the Paratroopers. I served with Admiral Halsey's task force in the South Pacific; with Lieutenant General Harmon's South Pacific Army forces; with Rear Admiral Wilkinson's Third Amphibious Force. I was with the Second Marines in New Georgia. I flew with General Kenney's Fifth Air Force in New Guinea and I was with General MacArthur's Sixth Army under General Krueger.

"My work was officially commended by Admiral Robert Carney, Chief of Staff to Admiral Halsey, and by Lieutenant General Harmon. I have their letters among my most valued souvenirs."

This 31-year old Brooklyn-born newspaperman joined the Mutual Network in 1945. It was for Mutual that he made his third trip to the Pacific, broadcasting from the headquarters of Admiral Nimitz.

PARATROOPER WHO FOUND HIMSELF

by W. W. Chaplin

Before dawn on D-day we landed 24,000 airborne fighting men behind the German lines in Normandy. They were the jumpers and glider men of the 82nd and 101st Airborne Infantry Divisions, and they made the invasion possible. Before the first landing craft had hit the beaches, the airborne boys had been through experiences that would make the war's most exciting book. Here's my favorite chapter:

The scene is a transport plane over Normandy, loaded with paratroops. The plane's door is open to a stormy night. The sky is dark, but through occasional breaks in the clouds the moon sends uncertain light. The jumpers are on their feet, each man checking with trained hands the equipment of the soldier just ahead of him. From the parachute pack on each man's back, a line runs to a cable strung the length of the plane. When the men jump, their lines will rip open their packs, release their chutes.

The jump master is a young lieutenant. He is responsible for getting all the men out of the plane, onto the ground and gathered together there as an alert fighting unit. His responsibility is almost unbearable. The lieutenant breathes like a man with a bad chest wound.

His wrist watch tells him the moment has come. He looks back for one last check. And he sees that the boy at the far end of the plane has somehow fouled his chute line. Cursing, he unhooks his own line, runs back and quickly, deftly, sets the boy right. Already precious seconds have been lost. The lieutenant runs the

140

They ran toward the spot where he must have come down. Soon they came upon a dazed paratrooper, sitting on the ground and holding his head.

length of the plane, shouts, "Follow me," and plunges out.

Only after he has gone over the side do the other men in the plane realize that in his excitement and haste the lieutenant has forgotten to hook his own 'chute line back onto the cable. The line will not open the falling man's parachute!

By every rule of reason the story should end right there: a tragedy, one of many on that stormy night. But it doesn't. By some miracle of contortion the jump master, realizing his oversight, practically crawled around in the air until he was falling face up, and tore his chute pack open. The silk streamed out, billowed full and broke his fall.

But our jumpers were dropped very low that night, just a few hundred feet above the earth, and when his 'chute took hold the lieutenant was almost to the ground. The parachute saved his life, but he landed with a crash that dazed him and left him 100 per cent "jump jolly."

Meanwhile, earlier jumpers already on the ground had seen him plummeting to earth. They had not seen his parachute open. They assumed that he was dead. But they knew that there was also a slim chance that his fall had been broken somehow, perhaps by a tree, and that he might be still alive.

The paratroopers ran toward the spot where they estimated the man must have come down. Soon they came upon the dazed jump master, sitting on the ground and holding his head, entirely befuddled.

"Hey, Mac," one of the men yelled to the lieutenant, "have you seen anything of a guy who came down without a 'chute? He must have landed pretty close to this spot."

"Without a 'chute? Good God!" the lieutenant said. "The poor guy. At that, it's possible he's still alive. I didn't see him come down, but I'll sure help look."

And so the hunt went on, until suddenly the lieutenant's mind cleared. He let out a whoop that brought the others running.

"I've found the guy!" he yelled. "It's me!"

W. W. Chaplin

William W. Chaplin left Brown University in 1917 to enlist in the Army. He spent two years in France as a doughboy, turned to journalism after his discharge.

He put in his early years on the Kingston (New York) Leader and the Syracuse Journal, followed them with 11 years of work for the Associated Press. He joined the International News Service in 1932 and was assigned to Washington.

From the capital he moved to the Rome and the Paris bureaus of INS and then reported the war in Ethiopia. Chaplin covered the western front in France until Dunkirk, escaped from the Continent and returned to this country.

He made a spectacular flying survey of the Pacific theaters of war, and in April, 1942, reported the Gandhi uprisings in Delhi. From India he was transferred to the Russian front, where he remained until November, 1942.

Chaplin joined the National Broadcasting Company the following year and in 1945 NBC sent him abroad to cover the final stages of the war in Europe.

Of himself, he says: "I am six feet one and a half inches, 140 pounds, odd looking and uneven tempered." He is the author of four books dealing with World War II: Blood and Ink, When War Comes, Seventy Thousand Miles of War and The 52 Days.

OLD SCHOOL TIE—COMMANDO STYLE

by John Williams

More than any other, the story of this one British soldier remains in my memory because, as you will see, it has no ending—yet. It started when his mother wrote me: "Three years ago I was afraid he was becoming effeminate. He wanted to go on the stage. ... See him and tell me what you think of him now."

I saw him just before the invasion of France. Two years earlier he had joined the Commandos. When we met, on his 22nd birthday, he was a captain and had been decorated with the D.S.O. Hard, supple, lean, he told me this story in clipped accents.

"I was a public school boy when we met last," he reminded me. "Four nights ago I was in France and I cut a German officer's throat. I did it without compunction. I was collecting preinvasion information and I wanted his personal papers.

"The French Underground is a marvelous show. The grapevine reaches into England, telling us where it is safe to land. Our destroyers put us ashore, and pick us up 48 hours later. We dynamite railroads, telephone systems and Nazi outposts.

"We got good training for this work behind enemy lines in Africa and Italy. I was a sergeant with eight men in my first show. We dropped at night on a Nazi airfield in North Africa. The Nazis are careless. One hangar was ablaze with lights. We reconnoitered and discovered they were holding a drunken celebration.

"We counted 40 pilots. Suddenly we opened a door and within 25 seconds they all were dead. We mowed them down with tommy guns, and to make sure, we tossed in grenades and set the build-

144

"Four nights ago I was in France, and I cut a German officer's throat. I did that without any compunction. I was collecting preinvasion information."

145

ing afire. We put delayed action bombs in all the dispersed planes we could, then fled across the desert to our own lines. That field was inactive for three weeks. They made me a lieutenant for that.

"Going into action, we wear camouflaged monklike robes with large pockets stuffed with grenades, automatic pistols, knives and bullets. We don't carry food; we live off the land like animals. We drop in a row from the belly of a bomber like peas from a pod. The first man stands still on landing, and those who follow move back to find and join him. After assembling, we advance in the darkness, close together, caterpillar fashion.

"Most of the men are between 30 and 35. We draw them from the London docks and they are tough. I have one as a bodyguard and he must not leave me under any circumstances.

"My next big job was when they dropped 12 of us behind the Nazi lines in Italy. Our mission was to destroy trains, and we dynamited three. Then we were all captured — but later we all escaped, after killing our guards. For six weeks we lived in nearby mountains and when the snow thawed we contacted an American outfit in the lower hills.

"After that, I was assigned to missions in France. I regard that work as relatively simple, because instead of parachuting we step ashore from boats, like tourists.

"Between missions we rest in special Commando camps in England, segregated from the rest of the Army. We can order anything we want, from chicken to champagne.

"But I spend a lot of my time at my bodyguard's home in a London dead end where too many human beings have lived on the bread line for generations. Before the war I did not know such people existed. There is justification for killing if this war will relieve the social congestion in the dark places of England. But if we don't follow through with reforms, the dead will haunt us. We talk about it between missions."

Remembering his gentle, aristocratic mother, I asked the boy only one question: "Do you tell your mother these details?"

"I'm all she has left," he said quietly. "Pater died from World War I gas effects. Felix [his brother] was shot down over Ger-

146

many. Margaret [his sister] was killed in an air raid. Mater is terribly brave. I wish I had her courage. There is so much ahead. . . ."

Then he answered my question. "Yes, Mater knows. She launders my bloodstained clothes and presses them faultlessly, especially my D.S.O. ribbon. You'd think I was going to a dance. And each time I leave, she calls down the garden path: 'Good hunting, my boy!' "

John Williams

for the Government, in Washington and elsewhere.

John Williams, who has crossed the equator 18 times, has spent the past 20 years traveling throughout the Pacific as a photographer and writer. During that time, he has worked for the Honolulu Star Bulletin, *for various Australian papers and as a free lance.*

In 1939, Williams, a New Zealander, became Hawaiian correspondent for Newsweek. *Eight years before Pearl Harbor he had insisted upon the inevitability of war with Japan and warned of her imperialistic ambitions. On a bitter December morning in 1941, Williams and his Wisconsin-born wife stood outside their home in Pearl Harbor and watched his prophecies come true.*

Later he came to the United States and performed confidential duties

THE KID FROM CONNECTICUT

by Charles Clapp

The Army Air Forces' England-based fighters were escorting the big bombers over Continental Europe one day when suddenly the sky was full of Focke-Wulfs.

It was a hell of a fight. Fighters crisscrossed the sky as they dived, zoomed, twisted, turned, flipped over and dived again.

Out of this mad maelstrom came, in a steady dive, a little Italian-born fighter pilot, August V. DeGenaro, his P-47 Thunderbolt full of holes. Lieutenant DeGenaro had had a very tough fight, had finally destroyed one enemy plane, only to find another on his tail, pouring lead into his plane—and into him.

DeGenaro dived to about 500 feet, then leveled off and headed back for England "on the deck." Both hands and both legs had been hit. DeGenaro was bleeding profusely, and he had a hard time keeping his powerful fighter on its course. He was losing strength with his blood, but he clung fiercely to one thought: he must get back to England.

As he came over the Channel coast he tried to put down his wheels to be ready to land at the first airdrome. The wheels wouldn't budge. His hydraulic system had been shot up.

"I'll have to crash land," DeGenaro decided. He wriggled in his seat to see if his safety belt was tight. It wasn't. It had come undone and lay limply across his legs. With bleeding hands he tried to fasten it. He was pretty weak by now and the task was too much for him. He decided he would have to bail out.

But where? A man can't turn a Thunderbolt loose with an open

Almost blinded with pain from the wounds on his hands, he battered at the plexiglass above him trying to make an opening in the canopy.

149

throttle just anywhere. Very weak from his wounds by now, De-Genaro looked through bleary eyes first out of one side of the plane, then out of the other. Below him everywhere were houses. He couldn't bail out over a populated section where his crashing plane would kill civilians.

With difficulty, DeGenaro turned his plane full about and flew out over the Channel again. As soon as he was clear of land, he tried to pull his canopy back. It had been damaged by shellfire and wouldn't budge.

By now almost blind with pain, he battered at the plexiglass above him. Finally the canopy moved, and, using all his remaining strength, he opened it far enough for his small body to pass through.

But by this time DeGenaro was far too weak to climb up and out of the cockpit, so he turned the plane over on its back, leveled off, inched his way through the opening and fell clear. Barely conscious, he pulled the rip cord on his parachute.

Even the cold English Channel wasn't enough to revive the young pilot. He was about to be pulled under by his parachute's wet weight when a fishing schooner's crew saw and rescued him.

It was just in time. In another few minutes DeGenaro would have drowned. When he was hauled aboard it was evident he needed patching up, so the schooner put in to the nearest port, which happened to be Newhaven in Sussex County.

As he was carried ashore, Lieutenant DeGenaro regained consciousness. He murmured: "Where am I? Where am I?"

"Newhaven, my lad," the schooner's skipper answered.

"Oh, I see," mumbled the young pilot. "Then I'm dead . . . I'm dead."

"Poor boy, he's delirious," said the sympathetic skipper.

But the skipper was wrong. DeGenaro thought he was dead, and he had reason to think so—for he came from New Haven, Connecticut, and had never before heard of Newhaven in Sussex.

Charles Clapp

Charles Clapp—who has been a real-estate man and a member of the New York Stock Exchange — has written advertising copy, several radio scripts and magazine articles. He is the author of two books: The Big Bender *and* Drunks Are Square Pegs. *He was a fighter pilot in World War I.*

In 1942, Clapp entered the Army Air Forces as a captain. He flew as an observer with the Eighth Fighter Command, in England, being attached to Public Relations; later, as a major, he was transferred to the First Air Force and participated in Flying Fortress bombing missions over Europe.

Major Clapp has returned to civilian life.

Asked to tell his most amusing experience, Major Clapp wrote: "The time I had to act as 'stand in' for the Duchess of Kent during the rehearsal of a ceremony at which Her Royal Highness was to present the official crests to the former Eagle Squadrons. As the troops were pass-ing in review at this rehearsal, General Frank O'D. Hunter, CG VIIIth Fighter Command, arrived on the scene and strode up to me as he exclaimed: 'What the hell are you doing?' 'I'm the Duchess of Kent,' I replied. 'Well I'll be damned!' he snorted. 'I'd never've recognized you.'"

THE CORPORAL KICKS THE GENERAL

by George Lait

It was a blistering 120-degree day in July. The 9th Australian Division—war-whooping like Indians, bayonets gleaming in the sun—had just recaptured *Tel el Eisa* (the Hill of Jesus) northwest of El Alamein, Egypt.

With the hill they took several thousand prisoners, mostly Italians. The gold shoulder insignia of captured officers and the silver stars of noncoms glistened on all sides as grinning, dust-covered Aussies marched long columns of captives back to our lines.

Lying beside me in a tiny slit trench atop *Tel el Eisa* was Brigadier General (now Major General) Frank Milburn. General Milburn —along with Colonel John F. Hinton and Lieutenant Colonel Charles Royce—had been sent from Washington as a special observer to study the famous British Eighth Army in action.

Six times during the forenoon Stukas had attacked the tiny knoll where we huddled. And several times the Germans' bombs had fallen close to large herds of Italian prisoners, wounding many of them. By afternoon, however, the air assault had dwindled and the Aussie moppers-up were finishing their job.

Considerably rumpled, General Milburn and I crawled from our cramped little trench, stretched our limbs and started to walk toward the beach half a mile away. There, the Aussies were lining up 1,500 Italian prisoners to load them into trucks and transport them to a camp behind the lines.

We walked past a pile of Italian dead, the bodies stacked neatly atop one another like cordwood, awaiting a burial party. Several

Stepping up behind the general, the Aussie gave him a boot in the pants and ordered, "Come awn, Pasquale, 'op into line with your buddies!"

153

wounded, waiting evacuation, joked with us from under improvised sunshades as we passed. We gave these Italians some cigarettes and General Milburn chatted with them a few minutes, sandwiching official questions between pleasantries. No one other than myself, I'm sure, knew that he was a general. American uniforms and insignia were then uncommon in Egypt.

Prisoners were an old story to me, so I strolled off to find a bit of shade, leaving the General alone as he watched a single Australian corporal march past with 200 Italian prisoners.

Hardly had I left his side when he was spotted by the corporal, who saw only a man in a non-British uniform wearing a silver star on each shoulder. Italian noncoms wear stars decidedly similar to those the brigadier was wearing. . . . What the hell, this bloke must be an Eyetie!

The Aussie, therefore, stepped up behind General Milburn, gave him a boot in the seat of the pants, snatched the two stars off, as was customary in such cases, and ordered:

"Come awn, Pasquale, 'op into line with your buddies!"

The startled American general frowned, then smiled and fell in. I looked up, and there he was—standing in the prisoners' line.

I rushed over and began to sail into the corporal, but General Milburn interrupted me.

"It's a natural mistake, Lait," the general said. "Forget it. I enjoyed it. Wanted to see what would happen."

The crestfallen Aussie tried to return the general's shoulder stars, but Milburn chuckled:

"No—you keep 'em, son. You wanted souvenirs; you've got 'em."

That evening, as we sat over steaming cups of tea and slapped at flies, the corporal marched into our camp carrying his large-brimmed Australian campaign hat upside down. He saluted General Milburn smartly and said:

"Some souvenirs for you, sir—and thanks for the ones you gave me."

He held out his hat. It was filled to the brim with silver stars snatched from hundreds of Mussolini's noncoms.

I clamped two on the general's shoulders. They looked fine.

George Lait

George Lait has been wounded four times; he wears the European ribbon with three battle clusters and the African ribbon with five; he has been decorated with the Ethiopian Military Cross, the Star of India and the Star of Africa.

With the International News Service since 1924, this 37-year old ex-Chicagoan has spent much of his time abroad, covering London, Paris, Rome and Berlin. He arrived in England in November, 1939, and was there to report the blitz, the devastation of Manchester and Coventry, and the invasion scare. In 1942 he went to Africa, where he recorded the brilliant history of the British Eighth Army. Early in 1943, he transferred to the American forces and was afterward hospitalized and sent back to the States with malaria.

Lait was next attached to General MacArthur's headquarters in the Southwest Pacific. He remained there through the New Guinea campaign and landed with the first assault wave at Leyte in the Philippines.

In August, 1944, he took the training course for paratroopers and received his wings. He then became attached to the 11th Airborne Division as a paratrooper war correspondent. Shortly before the attack on Luzon, Lait was ordered back to the U.S. again where he was hospitalized for malaria and dengue fever.

155

We are indebted to the following sources for the photographs used in this book:

Acme Newspictures
Columbia Broadcasting System
International News Photos
National Broadcasting Company
Newsweek
North American Newspaper Alliance
Omaha World-Herald
Overseas Press
Paul Parker Studios
Press Association
The Blue Network
U. S. Marine Corps
Yank